THE **UPPERCASE** DIRECTORY OF ILLUSTRATION

*The hours it took to create this book are
all dedicated to my wonderful boy, Finley.*

JANINE VANGOOL

Written and designed by Janine Vangool

Copyediting by Correy Baldwin

Cover illustration by Jeff Rogers

Printed in Canada by The Prolific Group

UPPERCASE PUBLISHING INC
SUITE 201B
908 17 AVENUE SW
CALGARY AB T2T 0A3

uppercasemagazine.com • shop.uppercasemagazine.com

ALISTAR KHABULANI

WORK / LIFE

3

UPPERCASE

"*Illustration is a really big part of my life. It's my passion and it's my work. And even if I'm not working I'm thinking about it, so there's not really a balance between work and life. But I don't mind—it makes me happy.*" LEA VERVOORT

Contents

We Love Work

When the first edition of *Work/Life* was published back in 2008, UPPERCASE was a fledgling publishing house. In 2009, our eponymous quarterly magazine was born, growing into a celebrated publication with readers around the world. In 2011, the second edition of *Work/Life* was released and featured 100 international illustrators. It was met with much enthusiasm, not only from art and illustration buyers who appreciated the book's quality content and curated talent, but also from other illustrators and aspiring artists who were inspired by the stories shared within.

As an independent publisher, I often use the phrase "labour of love" to summarize my work ethic. I love creating books and magazine issues that are intimate collaborations with amazing talent from near and far. The fine folks featured in *Work/Life 3* are dedicated to their art and thrive on the challenge of crafting creative solutions. They are excited to share their stories and eager to work with you.

I am pleased to bring you the third edition of the UPPERCASE directory of international illustration!

UPPERCASE
PUBLISHER, EDITOR, DESIGNER
janine@uppercasemagazine.com

Why a Book?

In this age of social media and immediate likes and digital shares, one might be curious why the UPPER-CASE directory is a printed book. We flirted with a companion app to the release of the second edition, but ultimately the illustrators we love—and the clients they dream to work with—are firmly rooted in the tangible. Print on paper (and fabric!) and the making of things... our illustrators want to see their work reproduced and broadcast in a physical way.

Online portfolios, blogs and social media are all fantastic tools for self-promotion, but with a seemingly endless stream of new content (and uncredited Pinterest pins), it is difficult to know if one's illustration work is being seen by the right people. With the *Work/Life* directories, we send the book directly to art directors and art buyers to ensure that it arrives in the hands of the people our illustrators want to work with.

With the ease of communication via email and file transfers, art directors are not limited by geography when it comes to selecting the right illustrator for the job. Alas, this means that we don't often meet our collaborators face to face, so this book brings us all closer together through personal stories, insightful interviews and compelling images while celebrating the diversity of illustrative talents from around the globe.

The *Work/Life* series has developed into something even greater than a promotional publication—these books are educational, inspirational and beautiful; books that have value beyond just a directory of talent. Building on the reputation of the first two volumes, the *Work/Life* directories are guides to those in the creative industries looking to hire talent. For aspiring illustrators, *Work/Life* is an encouraging companion for those on this challenging career path.

FUTURE DIRECTORIES

If you'd like to participate in a future directory, please submit your details at uppercasemagazine.com/wl4. Thank you.

1

Cover illustrated by Darren Booth, 2007.

darrenbooth.com

2

Cover illustrated by Alyssa Nassner, 2011.

alyssanassner.com

3

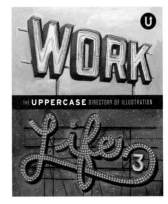

Cover illustrated by Jeff Rogers, 2013.

howdyjeff.com

An Illustrated Life

U nlike awards annuals or traditional illustration directories, our publication gets personal. Artists are individually interviewed about their creative focus and artistic technique as well as their inspirations and aspirations. Additional imagery documenting each participant's studio, process and inspiration are integral to each spread, allowing the reader to take a peek into their work/life.

With the third edition, we pushed the personal nature of *Work/Life* to a new level. This edition's theme is "An Illustrated Life", in which we explore the illustrator's lifestyle in intimate detail and find out what it takes to stay creative 24/7.

Each illustrator was given a detailed questionnaire containing 30 questions. From simple queries such as "What inspires you?" and "What is your ideal day?" to those requiring more introspection:

- *Has being an illustrator affected your personal life (ie the choice of where or how you live?)*
- *Where do you work? Do you have a studio at home or somewhere else? How does your workspace enhance or hinder creativity?*
- *How is your creative vision expressed through your work?*
- *What is your benchmark for success?*

After evaluating the answers and examining each participant's illustration style and desired clients list, UPPERCASE editor Janine Vangool crafted an illustration assignment specific to each illustrator's interests and personal story. It was an incredible creative challenge to come up with 100 different assignments, but the result is 100 original illustrations that best highlight our illustrators' unique talents. The full page image that each person created not only shows off their illustration style, but also reveals aspects of their character.

As a whole, this collection of illustrations is a picture of an illustrator's life: a summary of hopes and career dreams; the details and challenges of the hard work required of the self-employed; the importance of family in an often solitary profession; and the pure joy of expression.

KAL BARTESKI

OPPOSITE PAGE: OANA BEFORT RIGHT: VICKY HEALY, PHOTO BY LIZ CALVI

Making a Mess

Though many illustrators use digital tools to create their images or at least clean them up, making art means making a mess. The battle between clean and chaos is a common element with many of our illustrators, particularly for those who work from home.

"It's a disaster half the time because when I am prepping for a show I am usually building stuff on my desk, or dining room table or anywhere I can find space," describes Michelle Romo about working from home.

Diana Schoenbrun constructs her puppets and illustrations, so being messy is a necessary by-product of making. "I often make a mess and have to clean up every few days. It's a vicious cycle. But messes are productive."

In contrast, Michael Byers' environment affects the creative tools and methods he is willing to explore. "I work from the spare room in our apartment. It's all the room I need, but I think the only thing about it that I feel hinders me is the fact that I don't feel comfortable really exploring other media that might make a mess. I feel like if I had external studio space that was purposed for that then I might feel more comfortable making a mess."

Danielle Kroll loves spreading out and being free in her process. "I make a big mess. You can usually find me on the floor, surrounded by books and sketches on loose-leaf paper. I actually like to paint on the floor, too, it's more relaxing than sitting upright at a desk."

James Gulliver Hancock uses the word "messy" to describe his own personality: "Obsessive but messy, a duality and possible confusion of identity surrounded by positivity and interest in the world."

For many illustrators, the mess of creation might not only be a physical manifestation— it is also those swirling scraps of ideas that ultimately get sorted, culled and arranged into brilliant illustration concepts.

CHRISTINA LEIST

CLAIRE ISHINO

HELEN MUSSELWHITE

Process

"I start by thinking a lot before sketching. I stare into space. I flip through magazines. If I am in a rush I will brainstorm with the art director, throwing out any ideas, original or cliché. I write down words or doodle sketches on paper to spark associations and ideas. Using that as a starting point I start drawing in Illustrator. I will sometimes recycle parts of older illustrations to speed up the process. I'll move shapes around on the screen. At this stage there are often surprises that take the illustration a step further and make it mine. An association of objects, a crossing of lines or a 'wrong' colour can all contribute to the originality. And it wouldn't have happened in the earlier stages. So working on the computer is an essential part of the process, not only a technical step. I know it is finished when my time is up or when I'm happy with the result. Whichever comes first. "

JULIEN CHUNG

"Research is key. If an idea doesn't come to me outright, I often spend a lot of time trolling the Internet or flipping through books that inspire me. I'll go for a run, eat copious amounts of food thereafter (nullifying the run entirely) and make tea. Once I have a few solid ideas down, I begin to sketch and sketch and sketch until I am happy with the composition. Then I draw and re-draw until all the bits and pieces come together to form the final drawing, ultimately the base of the underpainting. I am, to my dismay, the ultimate tree-killer during this process. "

ILICHNA MORASKY

"My favourite thing about being an illustrator is the problem solving. I think because it is the most challenging part, it is also the most satisfying. Most of the time it is a slow, deliberate climb to find the right solution, but on the rare occasion that you can resolve the major issues early in the process, everything else achieves a frictionless flow. It feels like one of those dreams where you are running at top speed for what seems like hours but never feel tired or out of breath. "

LAUREN VENELL

LEA VERVOORT

Finding Balance

For many in creative fields, the lines between work and life often blur. It is a balancing act that is in constant flux; a windfall of work might be welcome for financial reasons, but it can interfere with one's personal life. Likewise, the everyday milestones of life and raising a family take time away from possible working hours. There is a constant push and pull of work and life requiring the illustrator and his or her family to understand and cope with the ebb and flow.

"I've always felt if you're doing what you love, it's less like work and more like play," explains Shelley Davies. "That being said, it's always a challenge to seek that perfect balance and I know nothing is ever 'perfect'. Ask me again when I'm 98 how it all went."

Lauren Venell maintains balance by creating a sense of order in a profession that can be very unpredictable. "First and foremost I employ a very robust organization system. If my brain space is being taken up by a to-do list, there's less room for more important things like creative problem-solving and sleep. I try to make long-term plans and not become a slave to the urgent. But creative work—especially for clients—doesn't tend to happen on a regular schedule. Setting rules for both the work and personal sides is helpful, such as beginning work by 9am, or committing to going out to dinner once a week."

Many successful freelancers abide by something similar. Having a daily routine can be helpful in maintaining perspective. Creating strong boundaries for family time is important, too. Though an illustrator might love getting lost in a project, the family might feel they're being ignored.

Vicky Healy observes that this career is very personal: "My work is my life but like any relationship sometimes you need a break to figure out where it's going. That's when I eat a lot of chocolate and catch up on my shows."

EMMI JORMALAINEN

JENNY NIEH

HELEN MUSSELWHITE

OPPOSITE PAGE: MEAGS FITZGERALD

" There is constant pressure to always be working and/or available, whether it be due to tight deadlines, manag-
ing and promoting yourself or simply wanting to push your work forward in new ways. I think it also comes
from enjoying what I do, so it is hard for me to not always be working or, at least, thinking about work. It takes a
concentrated and sustained effort to unplug and not neglect other responsibilities and relationships. It's important
and beneficial to make time for family and things non-work related and it's something I constantly try to achieve. "

BRIAN DANAHER

THIS PAGE: DANIELLE KROLL
OPPOSITE: EMMI JORMALAINEN

Work-in-progress shot of the cover illustration by Jeff Rogers. Jeff painted the day version of 'Work' and 'Life' and then transformed each into the night version by over painting.

THE DIRECTORY

Kelly Angelovic

BOULDER, USA

kelly@kellyangelovic.com
kellyangelovic.com

" **W**hen working on a project that I'm really excited about, I get this buzz—an electric current of excitement that lights me up from head to toe," enthuses Kelly Angelovic from her home studio in Colorado. "I am an illustrator because it makes my soul sparkle." Kelly's digital style is whimsical and sophisticated. "I am drawn to anything that's fantastical or absurd. It's so easy to take life a little too seriously (myself included)—so I enjoy anything that invites more fun into the game." She loves the power of colour and takes pleasure in selecting her colour palette.

Kelly's path to becoming an illustrator wasn't quite a direct one (she originally majored in business), but she has always been drawn to artistic pursuits. She muses that if she wasn't an illustrator, she'd be a dancer, a movie set decorator or costume designer. Kelly ran a creative studio focused on graphic design for a few years, but it wasn't until she became a mother that she discovered her true calling for illustration—while drawing during her daughter's naptime. "A new world opened up, and I fell head over heels in love with the art of image making," she recalls.

Juggling motherhood with freelance illustration is a challenge, but Kelly keeps it all in perspective: "I strive for passion over balance. My life is full, and there are usually not enough hours in the day. But if you love what you are doing, the energy flows and you can accomplish amazing things." Is there a benefit to being busy? "I no longer have the luxury of procrastination," Kelly laughs.

THE ASSIGNMENT

Draw a portrait illustrating this: "I get this buzz... an electric current of excitement that lights me up from head to toe. I am an illustrator because it makes my soul sparkle."

Lindsey Balbierz

BROOKLYN, USA

lindseybalbierz@gmail.com • @lindseybalbierz
lindseybalbierz.com

PHOTOS BY TOM TAKIGAYAMA

Lindsey Balbierz knows the value of hard work and a good education, attributing this appreciation to her mother who raised Lindsey and her two elder sisters as a single parent. "My mom put all three of us girls through private school and college while she was putting herself through graduate school. I think that is where I learned my work ethic and learned to always set goals."

Leaving her Cleveland childhood behind, Lindsey set her sights on New York City and attended Parsons' illustration program. Now, as a freelancer working from her apartment, a daily schedule lends routine to what can be an unpredictable profession. "My fiance and I used to share our second bedroom as our office. I since have moved to the front of our apartment where I can spread out and work amongst my books, sketchbooks, scanner, paints, pencils and inspiration board. I really like to be by myself when I draw so that I can get into my drawing zone. I like to make my studio like a cocoon."

Lindsey loves getting lost in her work, paying attention to the small details. "I naturally gravitate towards capturing details. I tend to dive into making my pieces really intricate with little narratives going on at different places in the image, creating hidden stories that people have to discover."

This ability to observe and concentrate is exemplified in a recent self-directed project in which Lindsey drew a portrait of a car every day for a month and posted them to her Tumblr. The result is a quirky collection of cars—and a documentation of an up-and-coming illustrator with a lot of drive.

THE ASSIGNMENT

Gather a number of significant objects from your personal history and illustrate them. Why are they important? What do they mean to you?

Emily Balsley

MADISON, USA

emily@bluestarink.com • *@emilybluestar*
emilybalsley.com • *bluestarinkblog.com*

Emily Balsley grew up in a small farming town in Northern Wisconsin. "If you're fortunate enough to dig through my parents' basement, you'll find boxes upon boxes of art projects, drawings and colouring contests my parents have kept since I was a little girl. Art has always been a huge part of my life, and spending time around my artist mother definitely helped foster that love for art. I can remember gently caressing her fancy coloured pencils or paging through her typography manuals—I knew that someday I would become a 'real' artist."

After studying art and design in college, Emily landed a unique job: designing bicycles for a Madison bike company. "Fortunately, my love of design and bikes led me to a new love—my husband. After we gave birth to a little girl, I decided to leave my job in the bike industry to spend more time with my daughter and explore other artistic opportunities."

With her daughter now in school, Emily is focussed on illustration—though her daughter's creative influence remains strong. "My daughter is a constant flurry of energy and ideas. I would love to channel some of those ideas into a picture book, inspired by her. My husband is a great writer, so a collaboration of the kiddo's ideas, my husband's words and my illustrations would be completely amazing."

"Many of my illustrations are based on my personal life, but I love the challenge of tackling new subject matter. I immerse myself in learning as much as possible, then figure out how I can spin it into my style. Some of my favourite projects have stemmed from unfamiliar territory!"

THE ASSIGNMENT

Ask your daughter to describe you and what you do during the day while she's at school. Use that description as the basis for a portrait.

Lesley Barnes

GLASGOW, SCOTLAND

lesleytoast@googlemail.com • @lesleybarnes
lesleybarnes.co.uk • lesleytoast.etsy.com

Colourful, complex patterns offset by rich blacks accentuate the mythology, fairy tales and folk stories that are recurring themes in Lesley Barnes' work. Equines are creatures that often figure prominently. "I have never actually been commissioned to draw a horse (hint hint!)," acknowledges Lesley, "but much of my personal work includes at least one equine character. I have never lost that small-girl fascination with shiny hooves, rosettes, dandy brushes and curry combs. When I was little my older cousin used to write and illustrate these amazing pony stories, and I think she really inspired me!"

Having lived in Glasgow, Scotland, and completed her studies there as well, Lesley has a strong connection to the city but is looking forward to experiencing other locales, such as London or New York.

For her *Work/Life* assignment, Lesley remembered the foxes that used to visit her parents' garden. "Even though the house is in the middle of Glasgow, it's near the park and gets a surprising number of wildlife visitors—mice, hedgehogs, squirrels, frogs and toads. A deer even jumped into our garden once! We used to have one special fox visitor. He came every night and would sit outside a window and stare at us through the glass. He would sometimes sit there for hours, his eyes glowing in the dark, watching us eat our tea. He also used to leave us 'presents' on the lawn—usually single leather gloves and odd shoes! I have no idea where Mr. Fox got them or why he left them in the middle of our lawn, but I like to think he left them for me."

"I love doing personal projects, as you have total creative freedom—I can indulge my love of folk tales, castles, knights and horses. It can, however, be a really good thing to have a specific brief, as it forces you out of your comfort zone." Lesley's dream project is to illustrate a children's tome of Greek mythology, or design a silk scarf for Hermes.

THE ASSIGNMENT

Create a composition of your own visual mythology, incorporating elements of your personal history.

Kal Barteski

WINNIPEG, CANADA

me@kalbarteski.com • @kalbarteski
kalbarteski.com • kalbarteski.bigcartel.com

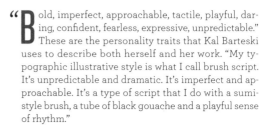

"**B**old, imperfect, approachable, tactile, playful, daring, confident, fearless, expressive, unpredictable." These are the personality traits that Kal Barteski uses to describe both herself and her work. "My typographic illustrative style is what I call brush script. It's unpredictable and dramatic. It's imperfect and approachable. It's a type of script that I do with a sumi-style brush, a tube of black gouache and a playful sense of rhythm."

Kal is prairie girl who headed east to study graphic design as a "backup gig" to her lifelong passion for painting. "I accidentally fell in love with design and typography, and how those ideas could melt together inside a paintbrush. Art, illustration and graphic design were my first jobs and will be my jobs until the end of time."

Through a positive online presence (blog readers will be familiar with Kal's popular "Link with Love" campaign, promoting responsible image use online), Kal has grown a successful business selling print and originals through her shop. She was recently a TEDx speaker and she complemented her presentation with slides rendered in her script style.

Working from a large home studio in Winnipeg, Canada, Kal's paintbrushes yield a diverse portfolio, from her signature brush script messages of affirmation and creative empowerment to studied renderings of vintage cameras and large-as-life polar bear portraits. "I'm a dedicated and driven chameleon. I have many styles and many different projects on the go at any one time. I am not swayed by trends. I am fearless and committed to my values and beliefs."

"I work best in my quiet studio, sitting on the floor. For script work, I do a million variations to explore what works best, but almost always end up using one of my first drafts. There's magic in things that are unrehearsed."

THE ASSIGNMENT

In your brush script render a phrase (or series of words) that expresses the joy you find in being creative.

Basemint

DES MOINES, USA

info@basemintdesign.com • *@basemintdesign*
basemintdesign.com

A ndrew Maahs and Kelly Bittner are a self-described "super-duper design and illustration duo" residing in Des Moines, Iowa. Inspired by mid-century vintage graphics and pop culture vernacular, their style is modern with a playful twist. As Andrew says, "We both have a sense of humour and don't take things too seriously. And as a result, we draw a lot of hot-dog-western-cowboys with holsters full of ketchup and mustard."

"We both had a passion for music and screen-printed gig posters. Nobody was doing that in Des Moines, not on a regular basis, so we decided to make some posters for bands touring through Iowa," says the duo, describing how they got their start. "After couple of years of producing gig posters, we started creating art prints and doing gallery shows. It has progressed from there to doing more traditional illustration work for clients."

Poster design informs the rest of their work aesthetic. "The process, textures and techniques involved with screen printing definitely makes its way into our illustrations."

Andrew and Kelly's ideal day includes bringing home the bacon as well as consuming it. "We eat some bacon, draw some stuff, maybe eat some more bacon, take a bike ride, visit a thrift shop and then finalize some projects." The pair firmly believe that although illustration is a business, creating things should ultimately be fun. They offer some good advice: "Don't grow up too fast. Enjoy the work."

"We have a hard time saying no to projects," admits Kelly. "We'll have time to sleep when we are retired."

THE ASSIGNMENT

Representing yourself as your favourite creatures to draw (Andrew: robot, Kelly: cat), create an overall composition with these characters in a stylized ultimate retro basement.

Oana Befort

BUCHAREST, ROMANIA

oanabefort@yahoo.com • @oanabefort
oanabefort.ro • oanabefort.com

Oana Befort lives in Bucharest, the capital of Romania, with her husband and young son. "My name is pronounced 'Wanna', but you won't offend me if you pronounce it a different way," she says warmly on her website. Fresh watercolours, florals, woodland creatures and her toddler Sammy are lovingly presented in light-filled photographic blog posts. "Photography is one of my biggest hobbies and it has helped me promote my work and add another level to it. It helps me capture the little details in everyday life, things that are a constant inspiration for my work."

Three-year-old Sammy has encouraged his mother's art pursuits. "My little boy definitely affects my career, but in a very positive way; he inspires me and gives me ideas just by watching him grow, learn and play. I worked in advertising for several years before being a mother, and after my little one was born, I made the decision to work from home. It's definitely not easy working from home and taking care of a little kiddo at the same time, but in the end I am doing as much as I can do and the best I can."

She keeps several sketchbooks to jot down ideas and doodles. "Running after a little toddler has helped me learn to think of ideas on the go, and it becomes easier to put them on paper when I get to stay at my desk."

"The best thing about being an illustrator is the freedom that I have in most of my works. This allows me to express myself and find my own visual voice. I am not sure if I chose to be an artist, really. I think I was created to be an artist. It is an integral part of who I am."

THE ASSIGNMENT

Create a portrait of your family, with each of you represented by a different animal that suits your personalities and temperaments.

Tammie Bennett

RED BANK, USA

tammie@tammiecbennett.com • *@tammiebennett*
tammiecbennett.com/portfolio

With schooling in journalism, communications and advertising, followed by law school, Tammie Bennett is a highly educated though self-taught illustrator. "I had my first child during the last year of law school and knew I wanted to stay at home with him rather than work in a firm. I felt a tremendous urge to create after having my son, so I started knitting, blogging, quilting, painting, and any other creative outlet I could get my hands on."

A business coach told Tammie to think of her 10-year-old self. "What did you enjoy doing?" the coach asked. "My answer was that I loved creating. I still love creating and I've realized it's okay to draw all day." She taught herself Photoshop and Illustrator, took online classes and began to document her skills on her blog.

A connection to childhood, through her own memories and now raising her three children, is integral. "There is a certain element of childhood that I will never grow out of and I think that certainly comes out in my work. You can see in my work my belief that no matter how dire a situation seems, things do get better. I like to celebrate the little quirks and nuances that make us all human."

Tammie challenges herself to hone her skills and creative thinking on a daily basis; even committing to posting a new surface pattern design every day for a #365 project. Her patterns are bold and cheery, ranging from abstract geometric to quirky representational.

THE ASSIGNMENT

Design the surface pattern for the featured fabric in your very own modern quilt shop.

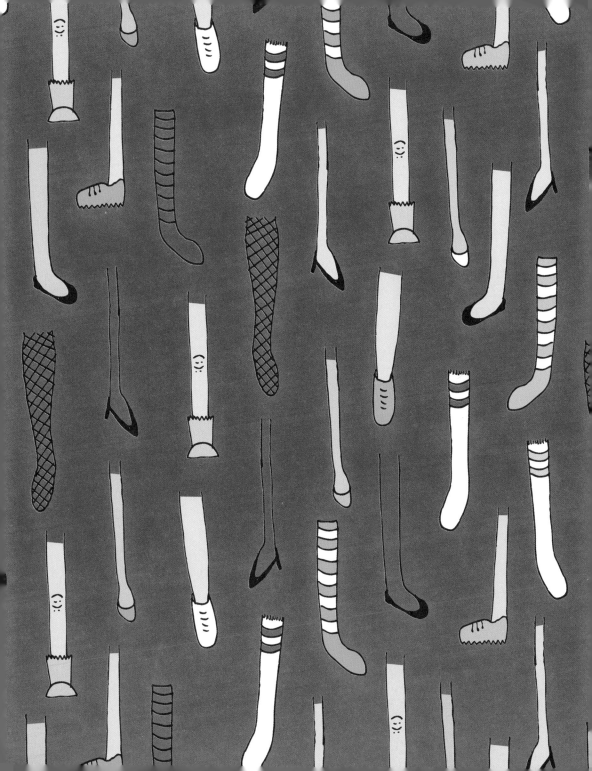

Vera Bertens

TILBURG, THE NETHERLANDS

vera@franjedesign.nl • @franjedesign
franjedesign.nl • etsy.com/shop/franjedesign

Dutch designer-turned-illustrator Vera Bertens can't imagine *not* being an illustrator. "I think that I see the world quite differently than 'normal people' do. Of course this is very common for anyone who owns a creative mind, but I like to see things prettier than they really are. I am a very optimistic person by nature and I see beauty in things that are not always commonly known as beautiful. As an illustrator I aim to make these things visible to everyone."

"Ever since I can remember, I was making stuff," she recalls. "I'm not the cliché illustrator who claims to have drawn ever since he or she could hold a pencil. Actually, I didn't draw much at all when I was a kid, simply because 'I couldn't draw.' Light, shadow and perspective are still a big mystery to me, which made me think for a while that I couldn't be an illustrator at all." It wasn't until her first year of art college that Vera learned that the ability to draw is not the key to being an illustrator. "This was the moment I cut myself loose of prejudice and just let my creativity flow."

Using a multitude of media, Vera mixes it up to create a style uniquely her own. "I have set very high standards for myself. The work I publish is maybe only 10 percent of everything I make. [Being a perfectionist] is a big part of who I am as an illustrator."

Vera lives and works in the same space. "You always take your work home with you when you have a creative profession, so there really is no going home from work," she observes. "When I'm working I'm not thinking about doing laundry or dishes, no matter how full my laundry basket or the kitchen counters are, but it doesn't quite work the other way around. When I'm not working while I'm home, I feel guilty about not working, even at nights or weekends." Though having an active, creative mind can get tiresome, overall it is this drive that results in great art. "You have a constant input of inspiration and new things you want to go do."

THE ASSIGNMENT

Using your illustrative dimensional technique, create a scene from your life—but imagine it as a shop window display or a still from an animation.

Ida Björs

STOCKHOLM, SWEDEN

ida@idabjorssuperillustration.se
idabjorssuperillustration.se

An ideal day for Ida Björs would go something like this: "I'd get up, the children would be nice, they'd eat their breakfast without fighting and get dressed without fighting, and then they'd go to school without fighting and then I'd ride my bike to my office. I'd have fun work to do and the client would say, 'Hey, that's a really good illustration. You're so smart. Thank you,'" something like that. And I'd have to drink coffee in between, of course, and eat lunch with a friend or a colleague. Then I'd get home and my husband would have made us some super delicious dinner."

To add to that ideal day, Ida's dream assignment would involve something to do with the theatre, allowing her to pursue an alternate career in textiles and costume design. "I would also love to work with a magazine that has some brains," muses Ida, adding, for contrast, "and some magazines that are glossy and superficial."

Ida's illustrations are emotive yet considered, personal yet universal. They often involve a bit of whimsy or surrealism, resulting in work that is slightly off-kilter. "All illustrators have the opportunity to create things that do not exist in the world as we know it."

Ida describes herself as having a big nose, big eyes, big hands, and eyebrows that are asymmetric. "A head that's bigger than normal because there's so much flying around in there," she adds.

THE ASSIGNMENT

Using your inspirations of theatre, fashion and folklore, illustrate a scene from your daily life that is changed or made fantastical through illustration.

Leonie Bos

AMSTERDAM, THE NETHERLANDS

info@leoniebos.nl
leoniebos.nl • leoniebos.blogspot.nl

PHOTOS BY MARCEL VAN DRIEL

" Although I've been making drawings before I could even walk, I never thought about being an illustrator," says Dutch designer and illustrator Leonie Bos. "I don't think our little village library had the kind of children's books that would have encouraged me to even think in that direction." Instead, her architect father and stay-at-home mom encouraged and stimulated Leonie's passion for drawing.

"After I graduated from the art academy I became a painter, but when I got pregnant shortly thereafter I decided to change course. I taught myself how to design and build websites, knowing I could earn a living and still be doing something creative. After having worked for a year as a web designer, I was offered a job as a designer at a magazine. From there it was a small step to making the magazine's illustrations, from where things took off."

A few years on, Leonie is a mother of a 13-year-old daughter and 4-year-old son. Her calendar is packed with assignments—a sign of the popularity of her talent and a dilemma she calls "a luxury."

"My style is based on the simplicity and brightness of traditional printmaking techniques. I love to play with transparent and shifted colour areas or to add a bit of texture and jagged edges, giving it that handcrafted look that gives my design its accessible character. I feel an attraction to drawing buildings and repetitive patterns. But I'm thrifty when it comes to drawing people in my designs. I somehow feel without people my drawings have more independent strength."

Growing up, Leonie imagined her name would one day be published in newspapers. "I remember not knowing if this would be a good or a bad thing. Would it be because I robbed a bank or because I was somebody important? Now I know it's because of my drawings."

THE ASSIGNMENT

You describe where you live as "the prettiest square in Amsterdam". Please illustrate where you live and what makes it so lovely.

Sarah Bridgland

LONDON, UK

sarahbridgland@gmail.com • @SarahBridgland
sarahbridgland.com • sarahbridgland.blogspot.co.uk

" I don't really consider myself an illustrator," asserts Sarah Bridgland. "Most people know me for my intricate three-dimensional paper works, made up of typography and printed ephemera. My background is in fine art, and most of what I do involves working with galleries and making work towards exhibitions, art fairs and commissions for museums and individual clients." Sarah has used her techniques on editorial briefs for clients such as UPPERCASE magazine and private commissions for the likes of Terence Conran.

"Most of my work is self-led, and the creative process starts with me going out and looking for printed ephemera that I can work with. I tend to go to second-hand book shops, junk shops, car boot sales and flea markets. From this material I cut out the imagery that I find visually stimulating—graphic symbols, typography, punctuation marks, printed page borders, etc. Once I have a large collection of cut out shapes to work with I start to build my paper sculpture. It's a slow but organic process."

Sarah doesn't plan the final piece from the outset. "It's an improvisational process. Fundamentally, my work is about arranging and reorganizing space and creating a sense of balance between different graphics, typefaces, colours and textures."

"I spent many years living and working as an artist in London before relocating to the English countryside last year, via a brief period living in New York. I am currently working from a quiet studio deep within England's Peak District. I am about to embark on a great adventure as I am expecting my first child with my partner Adam Hayes, who is an illustrator."

THE ASSIGNMENT

Create a collage about all the adventures you imagine you'll experience with your child.

Jessica Brilli

QUINCY, USA

jbrilli@gmail.com
jessicabrilli.com • *mammothandcompany.com*

PHOTO BY KRIS SNIBBE

Underwood, Zenith, Brownie, Kodak—these are the brand names of a bygone era. Manual typewriters, rotary phones, film cameras and transistor radios—iconic vintage technology that is having a notable resurgence in popularity, not necessarily for function but for its form.

Jessica Brilli is part of this renaissance. "I like to go to flea markets, antique shops and vintage shops to find items that speak to me." Jessica paints with a contemporary eye. Representational yet impressionistic, her work balances the truth of an object with artistic interpretation. "I'm painting the objects that I find interesting in such a way that others can see their beauty, whether they like those objects or not."

"From a young age I had an aptitude for art, and it seemed a very natural path for me," Jessica says. "I started to develop my style in college, becoming more comfortable with a looser type of realism. Since that time, I've experimented with various subject matter, but always enjoyed evoking the beauty in everyday scenes and objects. Seeing my painting concepts come to fruition is always pretty moving. There's something special about getting the idea out of your brain and onto a canvas."

Jessica lives in in Quincy, Massachusetts, and works at the Radcliffe Institute for Advanced Study at Harvard University. "I design by day, and paint by night," she says.

THE ASSIGNMENT

Make a portrait of the object that would be the best visual metaphor for you as a person.

Jenny Brown

PROVIDENCE, USA

jennybrownart@gmail.com
jennybrownart.com

F antastical urchins, pods, eggs, barnacles and blossoms make up artist Jenny Brown's visual language. Reminiscent of the scientific specimens of pressed flowers in an herbarium, her collage paintings are documents of imagination and beauty.

Jenny combines clippings from antique greeting cards and books with gouache, pen and ink, and pencil for her compositions, which she describes as "a completely unique creature—a melding of plant and animal." Ironically, she is not a naturalist: "I'm a total city person in awe of and completely in fear of the natural world. I'm fascinated by flowers and their complexities."

"I've been an avid antique and paper ephemera lover since I was young," confesses Jenny. "Old movies, antique books, treasure chests and old photographs bring me great joy. My found materials inspire me to find a way to make something old 'new' and relevant again." Growing up in a military family, Jenny moved frequently and often faced starting over in new locations. "I've been lucky enough to have a pretty eclectic selection of life experiences that have informed my work. I'm an army brat, a Bennington graduate, I've spent time living in France, taken a stab at teaching at the college level and working in the corporate world."

Collecting and treasuring found materials creates a connection with her surroundings. "Knowing that I've been able to be moved around so much in my life and have always found a way to make the most of things keeps me going when I feel down—and keeps me pushing through my work when I feel lost."

THE ASSIGNMENT

Inspired by your love of florals, create a drawing collage that would be used in packaging and advertising for a fragrance sold at a retail location such as Anthropologie.

Michael Byers

HAMILTON, CANADA

mike.byers@rogers.com • @michaelbyers
michaelbyers.ca • levycreative.com

"The worst part of being an illustrator is that you never have a day off. The best part is that you can take any day off you want," says Michael Byers, astutely observing the dichotomy of the successful illustrator's schedule. "In my short career, I have quickly learned some valuable lessons. Hand your work in on time. Do the best you can do on any job, no matter how much you might not like it. Be personable and humble. Be confident in what you do, or don't do it."

His image-making process is fairly traditional, but the results demonstrate skilled linework, expert colour, dynamic compositions and Michael's confidence as an illustrator.

"I'll start by doing postage-stamp-size thumbnails to try to work out a composition and ideas. I then take some ideas I like and make them a little larger. I'll also do some photo referencing if needed. I try to think of dynamic and interesting ways to draw my ideas. Then I will make a tighter sketch of the ideas I want to send off. Once an idea is approved by the art director I'll print off the sketch at the size I want to ink it. I then do one, maybe two tighter sketches to get to where I'm satisfied to go and ink. Then I use vellum over top of the tight sketch, and ink on the vellum. Then I scan the vellum and in Photoshop I add any colour and textures needed."

Michael keeps two separate notebooks. "My journal is more of a gratitude book where I record the things I'm grateful for. My sketchbook is where I practice, draw out ideas that enter my mind and work out what I'm doing for assignments."

"If I were to illustrate a self-portrait it would be a line drawing with some bright colours, and I would definitely exaggerate the glasses and the beard. It would be fun and full of animals."

THE ASSIGNMENT

Draw a whimsical self-portrait incorporating aspects of your personality and inspirations.

Cachetejack

VALENCIA, SPAIN

cachetejack@gmail.com • @cachetejack
cachetejack.com • cachetejack.tumblr.com

Cachetejack are Nuria Bellver and Raquel Fanjul, a Spanish illustration duo based in Valencia, Spain. The duo met at university eight years ago, but only began working together a couple of years ago. "Friendship, humour, irony, colour and energy is what put us together. We make decisions and have fun during all day. Our hobby is our work so we just have fun as much as possible!"

Their diverse output includes—but is certainly not limited to—books, magazines, newspapers, clothing, installations and paintings. "Cachetejack combines reality with a cool point of view," they explain. Personal biographies, hipster fashion and a sense of humour come into play. "Our style looks innocent, fresh, funny, cool, colourful and playful, but our concepts are serious, ironic and critical. So we may look like children at first sight but if you look a little bit closer you are going to discover a mature and honest personality."

They live and breath illustration and take the lifestyle seriously (though have fun while they're at it). "Being illustrators conditions everything. We have decided we want to do this for life. We put all our energy into it."

The benefit of working on a team is that neither Nuria nor Raquel ever feel alone, and they can share the burden of work deadlines. The drawback is the lack of a personal life. "What personal life? We are friends, we share a flat and we share a studio. We have almost lost our individual identities!" they jokingly lament. "For us, living and working is the same. We don't have timetables to separate them. We have the same friends, the same home and the same studio . . . but not the same parents! But now our parents are friends, too, thanks to us. The only things that are different between us are the clothes from our wardrobes and our boyfriends."

THE ASSIGNMENT

Sharing a career, apartment and studio could test even the best of friends. Illustrate a scenario depicting a real or imagined situation in which you would have a creative conflict. What is the conflict? How would it be resolved?

Maria Carluccio

DOBBS FERRY, USA

mariacarluccio@verizon.net
mariacarluccio.com

When illustrators are asked why they entered the profession, they often relate stories of their childhood. Maria Carluccio, whose creative pursuits have roots in her early development, is no exception.

"When I was young I loved to paint, draw and just play with all sorts of art materials—anything I could get my hands on. My mother was an artist, too. She encouraged me by putting me in various drawing and painting classes. I can remember when I first discovered that I was able to draw somewhat realistically. From that point on I knew I was hooked. I always thought that it was cool to be able to draw what you could see, but it was magical to be able to draw what you could feel or imagine."

"I've always loved to play with colour, shape and line. Most children have this curiosity and some never lose that sense of wonder. Playing is how we learn, as both children and adults. I try to approach my art that same way: enjoy the ride, let it take you to the places you need to explore. Whether it's a personal painting, an image for a children's book or a design for a quilt, I always want it to be infused with the random discoveries I make along the way."

Maria is in turn nurturing creativity (and the art of the critique) in her eight-year-old daughter. "She loves to tell me what's working and what's not, in both my art and just about everything else in my life. She has pretty good feedback in general. Recently we did a few art pieces together that my client bought as canvas reproduction images."

THE ASSIGNMENT

While imagining your dream of having your own brand of stationery, use your inspirations (nature, pods, flowers, colour, texture) to express your creativity and sense of style.

PHOTOS BY ELLEN CRANE PHOTOGRAPHY

54

we are all unique and beautiful.

Maria Carluccio

Mindy Carpenter

ASHLAND, USA

mindycarpenter928@gmail.com
mindycarpenter.blogspot.com • carpediempapers.com

"My life story could be called The Accidental Artist," says Mindy Carpenter. "I am a side-entrance artist. I'm the one who always worked in an artistic industry but was not necessarily making the art—approving it, sourcing it, marketing it."

Born and raised in Victoria, Canada, Mindy lived in Tokyo for three years and then "landed in the magical world of San Francisco and its lovely sister, Marin County." For a dozen years, she followed her passion for paper on the wholesale side of the gift and stationery industry, eventually finding her way to Ashland, Oregon. "I was seeking a change in pace and lifestyle, so in 2010 I made the move to Ashland to work with another kindred company in the gift and stationery world."

Mindy began to express her own visual creativity through art journaling. The act of painting resonated with her as she created nostalgic imagery of things she collected and held dear to her heart. "I'm drawn to single objects that evoke an emotion, like typewriters, rain boots or gourmet goodies in packaging. Things that make you feel good. I love animals wearing clothing, sail boats and all things nautical, as well as images that remind me of my childhood."

"My work is authentic. It's imperfect and wobbly but has a sincerity that resonates with people. It's a snapshot of colour and vintage appeal, and has a homespun folksy-ness."

Mindy recently launched her own stationery company, Carpe Diem Papers.

THE ASSIGNMENT
Paint a still life or a vignette of things you love in your home.

Alanna Cavanagh

TORONTO, CANADA

alanna.cavanagh@gmail.com • @alanna_cavanagh
alannacavanagh.com • alannacavanagh.blogspot.ca

Alanna Cavanagh showed artistic talent at a very young age. "I received encouragement early on when I won my first colouring contest at age six," she recalls. However, the performing arts vied for her attention as well. "After performing the lead role of Anne in a high school version of *Anne of Green Gables* I got bitten by the bug and decided to pursue a life in theatre instead."

Alanna sang, danced and acted for a few years but eventually went on to university to study art history and comparative religion. "As I began looking at art closely in my lectures, my love for it came flooding back and I began to draw again. After graduating (with no practical skills!) I decided to become an illustrator, as I loved drawing and design and knew I responded well to limitations and deadlines."

"I built up a portfolio and shopped it around and began getting gigs. In 1999 I signed up with an agency and after that my career grew quickly. I did work for many magazines, newspapers, design firms and ad agencies." A few years later she learned the craft of silk screening, a process she had long admired. Now Alanna divides her time between illustration and creating silk-screened art prints.

Alanna's work has been licensed for a capsule collection of home products at the Bay, the venerable Canadian department store—a thrill and a milestone for this Toronto-based artist. Her work has also been exhibited at New York City's annual SURTEX show, the biggest art licensing and surface pattern tradeshow on the continent. Alanna dreams of seeing her artwork and patterns on bedding, rugs and wallpaper.

THE ASSIGNMENT

Combine your love of entertainment, home decor and pattern design by creating a wallpaper inspired by your favourite show.

Alanna says, "My assignment was inspired by watching an episode of Mad Men *when the character Trudy picks up a bright orange telephone receiver."*

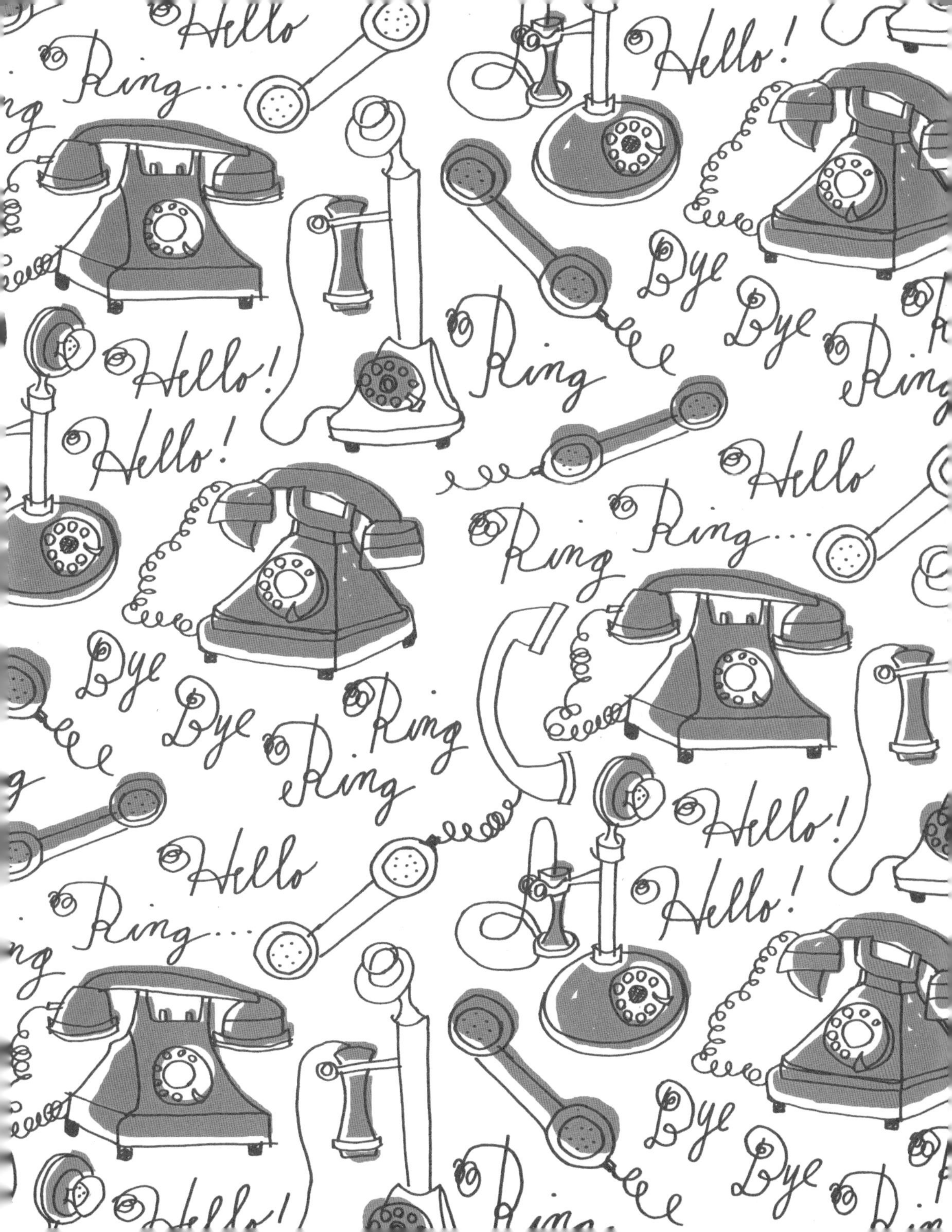
Hello!
Ring....
Bye
Hello
Ring

Nidhi Chanani

SAN FRANCISCO, USA

nidhi@everydayloveart.com • @nidhiart
everydayloveart.com

"I was born in Calcutta, India, and grew up in suburban California," says Nidhi Chanani. "I am your quintessential California girl. I love the beach, flip flops and good salsa. I also grew up in a big Indian family and I love the feel of Hindi on my tongue, elephants and big, bold colours. I married a white American man, and knowing him and his family has enriched my life. I live in San Francisco, and all of these pieces of my experience come together in my work."

Nidhi sums up her approach to art with her website Everyday Love: "I believe that every day there is a sweet, inspiring or beautiful moment in our lives." Nidhi's art—prints of couples, simple moments and San Francisco city scenes—evokes smiles and a few "awws." Her motivation isn't to present a veneer over reality, but to encourage a lifestyle choice towards positive thinking.

"When I started thinking about art as a career, I began with the thought of making people happy," Nidhi explains. "The world can make you sad, and it can be overwhelming. Originally I wanted to create political art, but my heart wasn't in it. As I started drawing more and heading in a direction where I felt comfortable, I realized that what I create is political. There is so much negativity in the world and art can combat it. It can remind us to stop, look around and see . . . that beauty is everywhere."

"Drawing from my background as an Indian-American and as half of a mixed-race marriage, I've been able to connect with a wide audience. Technology has allowed me to share my work with a global community. The response has been tremendous. On a daily basis I am greeted with emails and messages expressing appreciation for having created art that represents diverse communities, and work that delights and inspires. By pursuing this alternative path, I have connected with and mentored others who are interested in the arts or starting a small business, or who simply question the common path to success."

THE ASSIGNMENT

Illustrate a moment from your typical day when you are the most happy.

Alice Chiang

LONG BEACH, USA

aliceorz@gmail.com
alicechiang.tumblr.com • facebook.com/alicechiangart

Alice Chiang's drawings have a sweet, childlike quality that balances naiveté and sophistication. Using coloured pencils, acrylic and occasional collage elements, Alice's compositions are fresh, unfiltered and whimsical. "My style is pretty simple and straightforward," she explains. "Sometimes I just draw what I think, even if the images are not logically arranged. Colours are very important in communicating my ideas and constructing my work."

Growing up in Taiwan with two artist parents, Alice has always been exposed to colour and creativity. "My parents run a gallery and art studio, so I faced drawings and paintings literally every day." Her mother brought her illustrated children's books, planting the seeds for a future career.

"When I was in high school, I had to study all the time and was expected to choose a major that was more practical than art—just like all the other poor students in Taiwan. However, I watched Miyazaki's movie *Spirited Away* and I was so touched by the amazing story and art that I decided to go to an art school."

After an education in her home country, Alice was lured to the United States by the promise of adventure (and earning her MFA). She thrives on experiencing other cultures. "I like to observe a different city and see the architecture, streets and people. Now that I live in a foreign country, everything I see every day inspires me a lot."

"I like to try everything new, like surfing (struggling in the water actually), sailing, salsa, yoga—all of them are so difficult for me!—and even learning to drive a car and learning to speak like an American."

Her dream assignment would involve travelling the globe, documenting her experiences by making illustrations along the way.

THE ASSIGNMENT

Pretend that you have been given your dream assignment: to travel anywhere you want and illustrate the trip, all expenses paid. Where would you go? What would you see? What would you eat? How would you feel? Make a one-page journal page about your adventure.

Julien Chung

MONTREAL, CANADA

julienchung@hotmail.com • *@julienchung*
julienchung.com

Julien Chung is enjoying a diverse and prolific career from his home base in Montreal. "I started off as a corporate graphic designer, became an editorial designer and finally added being an illustrator when I hit mid-career. I felt I needed another creative outlet and a new set of skills in order to grow. I took a cartooning workshop and explored bringing characters to life by publishing a strip for a year. It all came together about ten years ago when I started combining my design sense and illustration with the desire to create products. That is when I started licensing, which allows one illustration to have many lives, like a cat."

Now that he's an empty nester, Julien is devoting his time to his licensing business. He offers various lines, themed for specific audiences. Woodland creatures, zoo animals, hungry robots and festive snowmen are the characters that frequent Julien's brightly coloured menagerie. "My style is minimalist, bright and bold, with a touch of whimsy. It is often described as modern with a sixties retro feel. I started the style a long time ago by cutting out paper, and now I use the same approach with the computer. I have simply switched the scissors with a mouse."

Working from his home studio, Julien is surrounded by inspiring books, past projects and things that make him happy. "I have organised it into four zones, one for work, one for archiving and storage, one for walking around in and the last one, which is my showroom for my products and also holds my library. There is lots of light and a nice view of the garden. I work best when things are organised with the least amount of clutter as possible."

"I like my art to enhance someone's day and I do that through my expressive animal characters, which appear on objects that can be found in the home, from a coffee cup to a wall sticker to a sofa cushion."

THE ASSIGNMENT

Using the zones in which you've organized your studio as inspiration, create an illustration of your studio.

my studio

Brian Danaher

ST. PAUL, USA

madeforending@gmail.com • @madeforending
briandanaher.com • briandanaher.wordpress.com

" I've been drawing and painting ever since I can remember and I always wanted to do something with art as a career, even though I didn't necessarily know what that was. I heard graphic design was a way to make a career out of being creative, and not starve, which sounded great. My first job out of school was at a small publishing company, where I was an art director for a B2B quarterly magazine. We never had an art budget, so I became the in-house illustrator out of necessity, which allowed me to try different illustration styles. This experience of working as both an art director and an illustrator has also been useful when working on editorial illustration assignments. When I moved on to agency work, I learned that the best, and sometimes only, way to sell a client on using illustration in a project was to do the illustration myself.

I work in a few different styles that can range from simple, bold, clean and iconic to something that feels a little more hand drawn and messy. Sometimes it is a combination of both. Regardless, I always aim to have a solid concept as the foundation for all of my work. Communicating an idea is more important than the execution of a style.

I used to have an idea of what a dream assignment would be but I've found that some of my best work has come from clients or industries that I had no prior knowledge of before working with them. As long as it is an interesting project where there is an opportunity to do something great, I'm interested.

Being an illustrator has made me more observant and eager to learn new things. I try to pay attention to even the seemingly insignificant details and moments of everyday life. Having a broad range of experiences and insights helps inform and generate new ideas. "

THE ASSIGNMENT

You've stated: "I'm inspired by people and/or companies who make things that are smart, relevant, useful and serve a purpose—things that make me want to spend time using them, both for how they are designed and for how they affect my life." Create a series of icons of food, products or other objects that make your life better.

MIND / BODY / SOUL

Helen Dardik

OTTAWA, CANADA

dardik@sympatico.ca • @helen_dardik
oneluckyhelen.com • orangeyoulucky.blogspot.ca

Helen Dardik has made up a word to describe her style: "toomuchery." But in this case, too much of a good thing is a good thing. Her work is exuberant, folksy, playful and optimistic. "I love the visual aspect of life," Helen explains. "I love colour. Love the emotion that I can convey with shape and colour. Love that it's always very personal."

Helen was born in Odessa by the Black Sea, lived in Siberia for a time and then moved to Israel, where she studied art and design. In the early nineties she relocated to Canada, where she found work as a graphic designer and illustrator. "I was a good graphic designer, but I am a better illustrator," she says. Her talents in both make her an exceptional surface pattern designer.

Her inspirations come from within. "I don't look for inspiration from others. I look to do something that I haven't seen yet. No one can copy what I haven't yet put out there."

"I have a studio in my home, but I mostly work in my head. Having the studio space white and clean helps to keep my mind organized, too. I have a lot of books—mostly design books and vintage children's books that I reference from time to time. I like to display my favourite things above my computer. Things we see every day do influence us, whether we want them to or not—so I like to have things that make me happy spread around the studio."

When asked why she became an illustrator, Helen's answer is matter-of-fact: "I don't think I ever had any choice. I was born to be an illustrator and that's that."

THE ASSIGNMENT

You say you were "born an illustrator". What if this were true? How would you have transformed or decorated your childhood?

Shelley Davies

VICTORIA, CANADA

shelleysdavies@gmail.com • shelleysdavies.com
shelleysdavies.wix.com/illustrations

" After attending too many art schools in my hometown of Toronto, I wended my way through many animation studios, making commercials, animated feature films and television spots—*Sesame Street* being a huge highlight. From the very tiny details of animation to the very large canvas of scenic painting, I went on to work in theatre, TV and the feature film industry. My Prince Charming came along, then two wonderful children, and a move to Europe for 12 years. I'm now back in Canada, in Victoria, B.C.

I'm creating editorial illustrations for magazines and newspapers, with children's book illustration at the top of my wish list. To have my work enrich the visual literacy of the world in any form, be it in book or magazine illustration, stationery, packaging or graphic design, gives me huge pleasure. Each little beautiful thing adds up into many beautiful things floating around the world, and I'm thrilled to add to that sum.

My creative vision is about play, spontaneity, colour and, most importantly, hopefulness. It's about creating my vision of happiness—not waiting for it to come along. And for me, creativity always comes out of the chaos, the mess and the grit of life.

I feel I've lived so many different chapters, with so many different facets to each one. With collage, there is no such thing as a mistake, only something tried—and if it's not the right fit, changed—just as in life. "

THE ASSIGNMENT

Design a collage for the side of a lunchbox, making it something your children would carry to school. The collage could relate to your life in some way.

Kristin deNeeve

SACRAMENTO, USA

kristindeneeve@gmail.com
kristindeneeve.com

Kristin deNeeve was born and raised in Hawaii, and got married at the age of 18. "I'm 32 and have been married for nearly 15 years," she acknowledges. "That really freaks people out!" Kristin received a BFA in Illustration from Virginia Commonwealth University and also attended the Illustration Academy in Richmond, Virginia. "After graduation I worked as a full-time graphic designer for nine years. In October 2012 my husband and I moved to Sacramento and I decided to begin my freelance illustration career."

"I don't have kids and have a very supporting husband, so I think I'm in the ideal freelancing situation. But I feel like I'm constantly at work, which can be stressful." Kristin makes a point of meeting up with other freelancers at least once a week and attends networking events when possible. "It's a good excuse to put on makeup and real clothes every once in a while," she jokes.

"If I were to illustrate a portrait of myself, I think I would look like a little kid—probably because that's how I feel a lot of the time, and I've always looked really young for my age. I'm only 5 foot 1, and I tend to work on a pretty small scale, usually nothing over 8 by 10 inches. I also gravitate towards small things for some strange reason."

"I like to paint things the way I wish they really looked— I wish there were a pair of glasses I could put on and the grass would always be bright green, and stars in the sky would actually be shaped like drawings of stars, and everyone would have these really big heads and look really funny. But then I wouldn't need to paint it because everything would look that way already."

Kristin dreams of illustrating a children's book. "It has always been my holy grail, since that's what made me want to be an illustrator. So I think when that happens, I'll feel like I've made it."

THE ASSIGNMENT

Being short-statured, you gravitate towards small things. Imagine you are illustrating a children's book about the power of small things and you are one of the characters.

Katy Dockrill

TORONTO, CANADA

katy@katydockrill.com • *@katydockrill*
katydockrill.com

" 'm still explaining what I do for a living," laments Katy Dockrill. It's a sentiment echoed by many professional illustrators. Though the community of illustration is strong, those outside of it often require more exposition on what an illustrator does on a daily basis. In Katy's case, she can recite the ever-growing list of well-read publications that have featured her illustrations and hand lettering: *Chatelaine*, the *Globe and Mail*, the *Wall Street Journal*, *Reader's Digest* and *Today's Parent*, to name a few.

Katy has been a freelancer for over 13 years. "I work from home, on the ground floor, right in the middle of everything. I'd love a cozier spot, but at the moment it works because I can be right there if my daughter Maggie needs me."

"Illustration is a full-time job. Motherhood is a full-time job. They are both important and require your full attention. It's not an easy thing to do, working job to job. Before having Maggie, I had every day, all day to live and breathe illustration. Now I have to really organize my day, and fit in all the things I used to do when I wasn't responsible for another person."

To aid in her concentration, Katy listens to music. "Listening to good music helps me focus my energy when I'm drawing and completing projects, especially when there are other things going on in the house. I've recently bought a better pair of earphones so I can create a little homey isolation."

Her dream assignment, she says, would go something like this: "Hi Katy, would you mind terribly taking a trip to Barbados to sit on the beach and draw anything you like?" While waiting for that call, Katy loves to swim and she reads as an escape from the everyday. "I play the piano to relax and I craft because I like to make things. Being creative in ways other than drawing keeps me sane and keeps my ideas fresh."

THE ASSIGNMENT

Using images and handlettering, illuminate your statement:
"I'm still explaining what I do for a living."

Kiersten Eagan

OTTAWA, CANADA

kiersteneve@gmail.com • @kiersteneve
kiersteneve.com • kiersteneve.blogspot.com

" I was lucky to be born into a wonderfully weird family who could create adventures out of anything, so there was never a dull moment! I was influenced by my grandfather, who is an incredibly talented artist, and my mom, who is a writer, so the creative atmosphere was always there. After high school I got a degree studying math but sketched my way through every class, travelled and then finally decided to set sail for San Francisco to study Illustration. I graduated in 2011 and have since moved back to Ottawa, where I am currently living and working.

For as long as I can remember I've wanted to be an artist. It all started back when I would bust out of my crib to go scribble all through the night, and not much has changed! Except the crib.

My curiosity and sense of wonder about the world translates into a lot of my images. People are always fascinating to draw because the possibility for storytelling is endless. I also love drawing different compositions and thinking about the power that elements like shape, size, value and position can have to communicate.

I love movies and books, which definitely relates to my career, because just like illustration they are about storytelling. Also, cinematography translates pretty directly into illustration in terms of composition and I'm constantly pausing movies to geek out over incredible shots!

Right now my career is definitely wearing the pants. I like to think I'm still fairly young and, with no kids or many obligations, I have the opportunity to really focus on my work, which is exactly what I want right now. Also I'm very lucky to live with an incredibly supportive and wonderful boyfriend who can entertain himself for long periods of time! "

THE ASSIGNMENT

Create the scene of you as a toddler, busting out of your crib to go scribble and draw in the middle of the night. Think of it as a still from a cinematic and moody movie.

Bambi Edlund

VANCOUVER, CANADA

draw@bambiedlund.com
bambiedlund.com

"Two of the things I love most are animals and facts," declares Bambi Edlund. "I think being a wildlife researcher—or rescuer—would have been a good alternative path for me. Wait, is 'raccoon whisperer' a job? If so, that would be a strong contender."

Possessing the talent to draw all her life, Bambi's path to becoming an illustrator wasn't something she consciously pursued. "I have been able to draw since a very young age, so in some ways I have been an illustrator all my life. There were periods where I didn't do it much, but there was never any doubt that I would end up as an illustrator. That said, being paid to draw things still feels like a dream."

Bambi excels at expository illustrations, getting into the mechanics of how things work, where ingredients are the heroes. "I love drawing detailed line drawings of intricate things: machinery, plants, vehicles, buildings. But when it comes right down to it, that's not what I draw. If I'm sitting somewhere, say in an airport or café with a pen in my hand, it's always animals that come out. They're often inspired by what's going on around me, but they're the fauna version—rabbits sipping coffee and carrying suitcases, pigs keeping an eye on naughty piglets, coyotes making angry calls from the pay phones. I have a multitude of sketchbooks filled with them. I love drawing these guys because I often don't know what they're going to be doing when I start. They sort of reveal themselves to me. It feels like I'm meeting them as I draw them."

"My style, in terms of the media I use, is kind of luddite-meets-tech nerd, which also could be said of me.

Up until recently, I mostly used dip pens and India ink on Bristol for the lines, then I would scan the drawing and add colour and texture using Photoshop and Illustrator. However, I recently acquired a Cintiq tablet, which is like a dream come true—I can replicate my usual thick-and-thin ink lines without having to worry about dragging my hand through the wet ink!"

THE ASSIGNMENT

Draw a field guide to raccoon whispering, telling the story of the urban wildlife in your city.

Cecilie Ellefsen

OSLO, NORWAY

cecilie@madebyceceilie.com • @cecilieellefsen
madebyceceilie.com • sailorlarry.com

" I grew up in a small town by the sea in southern Norway. As a kid I loved to draw, play the tuba, ride horses and make small forts in the woods with my friends. I used to smuggle out pencils and pieces of paper during recess at school and find a quiet place to draw.

When I got older I studied graphic design, moved to Oslo and studied art direction. After the financial crisis of 2001, I decided to pursue my dream of becoming an illustrator. I applied to art school here in Oslo to study illustration, but I did not get accepted. So I built up a portfolio and showed it to publishers and to ad and design agencies. I got offered a job as an in-house illustrator at a design agency and it all snowballed from there.

Since I never went to art school, I am used to a hands-on way of doing things. What I know of illustration, I've learned through working hard through trial and error. I've never had a 'this is how you illustrate' book or lecture, but on the other hand I've never been told what not to do in illustration, so maybe I think more freely.

I feel like a kid a lot of the time, and illustration is my never-ending playground. There is so much colour and life in illustration, and I love the feeling of immersing myself color and drawing new worlds. "

THE ASSIGNMENT

Take your comment "illustration is my never-ending playground" as the starting point for your illustration. Show yourself keeping busy and having fun in this creative environment.

Naomi Elliott

LONDON, UK

hello@naomielliott.co.uk • @nelliott
naomielliott.co.uk

" I was born in a sleepy village in Northern Ireland where I lived until I was 19. It was a very quiet place with not much to do so I kept myself amused with reading and drawing. I always knew I wanted to move to a big city, so after finishing school I packed up all of my things and made the move to London.

Since moving to London, I've always lived in the same area, as it's a really creative place and it's nice to live somewhere with such a great artistic community. It may not be the most desirable part of town for others but for me it's perfect. I try to go out once a day, even just for a walk along the street, so I don't feel too cooped up. There are lots of nice coffee shops where I can work from, too, which is nice for a change of scenery.

I am always looking for ways to make quite 'ordinary' things look more dreamlike. My vision is to make something quiet that requires more than a quick glance to get into. I take a lot of inspiration from books and dreams. Sometimes when I'm reading something, one line will really hit me and I can see that world so clearly, and it will spark something that I feel I need to explore. It's similar with dreams. I've always had vivid dreams, and I've kept a dream diary for a few years where I try to make a note when I wake up of what went on in those few hours when I was asleep.

My work is quite calm and controlled, which perhaps comes from my personality. Essentially, my style is quiet and simple. I like to try and limit my colour usage to one or two and to use different textures and patterns to bring my work to life.

The best thing about being an illustrator is making the things I see inside my head a reality and getting to do that for a living. "

THE ASSIGNMENT

"I always am looking for ways to make quite 'ordinary' things look a little bit more dreamlike." Make a picture that contrasts or compares what you see in your head and what you see when you walk in your Southeast London neighbourhood.

82

Mareike Engelke

DUISBURG, GERMANY

post@mareikeengelke.de • *@milkkid*
mareikeengelke.de

Mareike Engelke was born in.a small German town by the Rhine and spent her childhood in a florist's workshop. "My ancestors were gardeners," she notes. Always inventing, sketching and crafting, her teachers encouraged her to draw. "Luckily my teachers saw a context behind my drawings and encouraged me to focus on illustration."

"My illustrations are rough, funny, handmade, playful, raw, dense, multilayered," she says. They are primarily created with mixed media, such as pen, pencils, gouache and cut paper, then refined digitally. The results are very expressive, colourful and fresh."

"I roll the subject matter around in my head while I'm doing other things. I may be on the train, or taking a shower. I try not to push too hard until an idea forms on my inner eye," says Mareike, describing her creative process. "Then I consider the materials that I like to use, which I tend to want to use all at once. My ideas are like a theatre troupe and I need to choose just some of them."

"There is a strong connection between my illustrations and my personality and the experiences I have had," she says. Though the connections may at times be subconscious and hidden from Mareike, her friends often remark on them.

"I like to draw hairy men. That's why everyone thinks my husband must be very hairy. He isn't. It's just fun!"

THE ASSIGNMENT

Honouring your gardening ancestry, create a portrait or scene about growing up in a flower shop.

Lucy Engelman

GRAND RAPIDS, USA

engelucy@gmail.com • @lucyengelman
lucyengelman.com • lucyengelman.tumblr.com

" I grew up barefoot and frolicking in the muddy woods just outside Chicago, where my imagination, rooted in the woodland, became the thing I covet today. I attended the University of Michigan, roaming the quirky streets of Ann Arbor where I strayed from the safe bounds of illustration into the endless possibilities of a liberal arts university. After college, I returned to Chicago and threw myself into becoming a freelance illustrator.

When I was first starting out, I was incredibly driven to succeed and pushed myself too hard. I spent months working as long as I could keep my eyes open, until I hurt my hand. I had no personal life because I was so focused on my career. It took a doctor telling me I needed to slow down for me to understand that as great as success is, it isn't worth hurting yourself and shortening your career. Happiness comes from a balanced life.

At this point I hadn't made anything for myself in over a year, so I signed up for a residency called Cabin Time. No work, remote camping in the woodlands of Minnesota with a bunch of workaholic artists like myself, and my eyes were opened. Creating that wonderful network of friends and colleagues motivated me to move to Grand Rapids, Michigan, where I now spend my days still working hard but my nights exploring what they call a personal life. I hope to travel and expand the network of friends and fellow makers I've started to collect, and live all over. That's what's so great about being a freelance illustrator—the possibilities are endless. "

THE ASSIGNMENT

Create an illustration about your Cabin Time residency, using narrative text and handlettering along with your illustrations to share the experience with our readers.

Extracurricular Activities

PASADENA, USA

vcying@gmail.com • @victoriaying
eca-design.com

PHOTOS BY EVER WHIM PHOTOGRAPHS

Mike Yamada and Victoria Ying are a married couple living in Southern California. They met at a party for artists—sketching in each other's sketchbooks. Both have since worked on numerous animated features and shorts for DreamWorks Animation and Walt Disney Animation Studios. As Extracurricular Activities Design Studio, they combine their talents to work on books and animation.

There are benefits to having a shared career: "Having a spouse who does the same work allows us to be more understanding towards each other when work gets crazy," agree Mike and Victoria. "Work and life have always been very intertwined. I don't know if balance is what we strive for, but we've found a place that we are happy with."

Their ideal day would go like this: "Waking up, making a cup of coffee, reading a magazine while we drink and chat, and then splitting up and working, coming back around lunchtime to talk about what we have been doing and going out for a cold beer, then coming back to work some more, having another meal and then watching *Game of Thrones!*"

Victoria's dream is a little risqué. She's always dreamed of being in *Playboy* and doing a cartoon for them, since some of her biggest heroes were *Playboy* cartoonists, including Dan Decarlo and Kiraz.

Mike has always wanted to do an illustration for *Wired*, and together they would love to do a "Little Golden Book."

THE ASSIGNMENT

Draw a portrait of each of you working in your separate studios, with the middle of the page being the point where your creativity comes together and blends or interacts.

Meags Fitzgerald

MONTREAL, CANADA

meagsfitzgerald@gmail.com
meagsfitzgerald.com • photoboothabiography.com

PHOTO FAR LEFT BY ARISTA LEGER

" My childhood home in Edmonton was filled with activity. With two older sisters and two younger brothers, I always had playmates and was able to retreat unnoticed into my own made-up worlds. There wasn't a precedent for creative-types in my family, but my parents were supportive of my talents. I attended an incredible performing and visual arts high school. I completed a BFA at the Alberta College of Art & Design in Calgary. After graduation I went on tour, performing and teaching improv theatre in North America, Europe and Australia. Travelling forced my artwork to take on new forms; portability was key. Having relocated to Halifax, with a new interest in illustration, I studied design at the Nova Scotia College of Art & Design. I've been doing freelance illustration ever since.

Drawing was the first thing I was good at, I just always knew I was going to be an artist. When I finished my BFA, however, I was surprised to find that, despite loving the process of making art, I was not attracted to the artist lifestyle. It felt too solitary and insular. Books have always appealed to me because they can be appreciated anywhere at anytime by anyone, unlike an exhibition in a gallery. I've dedicated the last two years to researching, writing and illustrating a graphic novel, *Photobooth: A Biography*, which will be out with Conundrum Press in spring 2014.

If I were to draw a self-portrait, it would be a collection of things essential to me: my cat, a cup of tea, my sewing machine, a stack of photobooth pictures, a heap of books, some chocolate, with my hands working on something. I'd sneak in nods to my family and friends, too, through my choice of items. "

THE ASSIGNMENT

Draw a view of your desk featuring items of biographical importance.

Yael Frankel

BUENOS AIRES, ARGENTINA

yaelfrankel@hotmail.com
yaelfrankel.com

Yael Frankel was born in Buenos Aires, Argentina. She was the youngest of four children, and loved to draw, collage and paint. "Now I am a graphic designer and illustrator, I am married and have two great children and still love to do the same things with my hands."

"I discovered my love for illustration while I was working as a graphic designer. I realized that I was including my own illustrations in packagings and brochures, and that my clients were happy with them." Her work has a naive, innocent sensibility: "I think that they reflect my inner child, my concerns and my playful side. I am often willing to explore my questions and doubts, and to try to capture them in my work." She loves picture books and excels at telling simple stories imbued with a sweet innocence or light melancholy.

"Illustrators are very detailed, they are observers more than active participants, solitary, nice people, I think," says Yael. For her, the best thing about being an illustrator is the ability to speak without words—although that can also be a cause of anxiety at times. "There is the possibility that someone might not understand what we are trying to say."

Her ideal day involves waking up early and heading to her studio to have breakfast. When feeling inspired, she illustrates without noticing the hours passing by.

Now that her children are maturing, Yael is dedicating more and more time to her art. "I can do what I love the most: travel to take illustration workshops around the world!"

THE ASSIGNMENT

If you were to make your childhood into a picture book, illustrate a moment or memory (real or imagined) in which you felt most unique or different from your three other siblings.

Janet Freysoldt

MONTREAL, CANADA

contact@janetatwork.com
janetatwork.com • be.net/JanetatWork

B orn and raised in Germany, Janet Frey-soldt studied media design in Weimar and worked for a few years as a cartog-rapher before meeting the love of her life at a conference in Berlin. She followed him to Paris and went on to Brussels as an exchange student. After spending more years in Paris, the couple moved to Montreal, Canada, where they live with their two children.

"I have a day job where I sit in a white cubicle inside an office. I think all the walls in the of-fice most likely hinder creativity, but I walk around, talk to people and look out of the win-dow to get inspiration." For now the stability that a day job affords is important. "If I didn't have kids, I would take many more risks and work as a freelancer full time. Working from home and being my own boss is what I want to do in the long term, but I want to be very well prepared first. I am more hesitant be-cause my family depends on my income."

Janet loves the challenge of commissioned illustration. It offers her the chance to look at something from a different angle. Her style is isometric, detailed and clean, but far from clinical. She always has a sketchbook or pa-pers close at hand to jot down ideas and notes of things to focus on.

"I very much like the flow of life and how you don't know where it will take you. I am open to whatever comes next."

THE ASSIGNMENT

Create an information graphic or series of graph-ics depicting the places you have lived, referencing the personal stories that make these places special to you.

Work/Life

Holzthaleben

Weimar

Brussels

Paris

Montréal

Scott Gandell

SOUTH PASADENA, USA

scottgandell@gmail.com
scottgandell.com • spmercantile.com

Scott Gandell doesn't work from home or from a typical studio, but rather from the South Pasadena Mercantile Co., a space that he co-owns with his partner, Anneline De Croos. "It's at once an interior design showroom, retail space, museum and art gallery. It's a space that's meant to engage visitors and hold their attention."

Being in a public space and engaged with customers gives Scott a unique perspective on his own art. "My daily experiences at work and interactions with others inherently inform my ideas. I'm able to promote illustration and expose others to it, and educate them with my personal experiences in the business and the history of illustration—people who otherwise would not have had access to illustration or an understanding of it, but can now gain a sincere appreciation."

"I've been able to carve a niche of studio space at the South Pasadena Mercantile Co. that allows me to work throughout the day and into the night." The diversity of the space and its activities offer the variety that Scott craves. "My capacity for sustained attention is limited, so the speed at which I work allows me to engage my daily muses. The atmosphere of South Pasadena Mercantile Co. enhances my creativity and allows me to create more engaging and persuasive illustrations by paying attention to how people listen, decide and react."

Scott collects toys, books and art. "These objects offer creative escape, inspire my dreams, elevate my professional goals and enrich my craving for more of the same."

THE ASSIGNMENT

Illustrate a selection of special items from your collection of toys, with brief descriptions of why they are special to you or of particular note.

when I was just a
little boy I crop
dusted every inch
of the floor with
my toys—now I
just fill the nooks
and crannies with them.

scott gandell

Chad Geran

REGINA, CANADA

chad@geran.ca • @chad_geran
geran.ca

"When I meet people from outside the creative industries they often ask, What do you do for a living?" says Chad Geran. "I say, I'm an illustrator. They often smile and nod, and I can tell they have no idea what that really means. Usually, I clarify it by saying, I draw cute pictures of animals, for money."

Chad is an illustrator with a background in graphic design. "My graphic illustration style has been strongly influenced, I believe, by the many logo projects I've worked on. I enjoy the challenge of reducing images to their essentials. I'm interested in shapes, the relationship of positive and negative spaces and the mood one attempts to create with colour."

Drawing on the appeal of mid-century aesthetics, Chad's work is characterized by its retro simplicity. "I like the reduction that happens during the process of creating silkscreen-printed images. These interests, along with my animation training, have certainly influenced a retro-inspired graphic style."

Chad works from his home in Regina, Saskatchewan, though his tools and laptop are perfectly portable: "In the past year, my favourite work spot was the balcony of a beachfront back in Whangamata, New Zealand. The control of my own time and location was a big part of my decision to freelance full-time. I often work while travelling with my wife and son."

Chad credits becoming a parent to giving structure and a helpful schedule to his life. During ideation for his *Work/Life* assignment, Chad explored how his child is now in charge of his life. "In my sketchbook I wrote 'In our house, Brin is the centre of the universe.' As you'll see, I've shown a universe contained by the shape of a house, with my son in the centre."

"As a dad, I'd love to work on a children's book. I see so many books that I feel could be so much more stylish and interesting for kids."

THE ASSIGNMENT

You wrote, "Having a son put a schedule and structure into our lives." How else has he changed you? Create a humorous illustration showing how your child is in charge of your life.

PHOTOS BY CAREY SHAW

Gomez Illustration

MADRID, SPAIN

toctoc@gomezillustration.com • @gomezdrawings
gomezillustration.com • gomezillustration.tumblr.com

Ana Gomez Hernandez's creative process starts with a morning walk. "I go to my favourite café, get a coffee and a croissant, and think, think, sketch, think. Then I walk all the way back to my home studio, still thinking." By the time she gets to her home studio and sits down in front of the computer, she's ready to draw.

Ana used to work in an office, but one day she saw a contest advertised on the Internet. "The next thing I knew, I had won a scholarship to the Istituto Europeo di Design in Milan for three months, complete with an apartment and €1,000 a month. Wow! Imagine my face at the office. I quit."

Though she enjoys her illustrator's life, working from home can get lonely. Ana enjoys the companionship of her son when he gets home from kindergarten. "I had a shared studio outside our home before, but with the birth of my son I had to save time and money. In the evenings I love to share my studio with him. My mood is better and is reflected in my illustrations."

Drawing her colourful invented characters, called Murs, puts Ana in a good mood. With their big eyes, smiling faces and simply shaped bodies, these characters express a carefree happiness and epitomize the innocent curiosity of childhood. Whether they're riding a bike, sharing a picnic or exploring shapes and colours, the Murs are creative companions that engage her imagination.

THE ASSIGNMENT

A drawback to being an illustrator can be loneliness. Draw the cast of characters that keep your imagination from being lonely and keeps your mind busy. What do they do to keep you inspired and motivated? What kind of world do they exist in?

James Gulliver Hancock

BROOKLYN, USA

james@jamesgulliverhancock.com • @gulliverhancock
jamesgulliverhancock.com • allthebuildingsinnewyork.com

" I n a typhoon in the sea between Japan and Vladivostok I remember thinking, 'I'll save my sketchbook if we're shipwrecked,'" recounts James Gulliver Hancock about a voyage he took through Asia, Russia and Europe. "Drawing has always calmed my nerves and made the world make sense." James, who was born in Australia, made his way to New York City, where his illustration career set sail.

"Right now I'm working in my home studio, lavishly set up with multiple desks and room to make whatever kind of drawing and mess I want. It's connected to the house in such a way that it's private, but I can be connected to the goings-on. But I also keep a studio in Brooklyn, sharing a space with other like-minded people. This is super important and they are people who I've come to love and whose work I respect hugely. I've learned the most about my career from having that space."

"I have worked towards a career that both allows me and makes me move around a lot. I love moving studios and working in different environments. Being based between New York and Sydney means I see a lot of the world and work with people all over it."

He appreciates how his career allows for personal time. "I'm very lucky that I get to spend a lot of different types of time with my son. I'm not stuck with only seeing him in the evening, like with office work."

James also doesn't get stuck on one particular media. "I mix up my media. Pencil and paper are obviously key fathers of every project, but I love being in a jam and using what is at hand—whether that's a feather and ink found on a plain in Australia, or a drafting table and mechanical pencil in my perfect studio."

THE ASSIGNMENT

Create a portriat that creatively documents your own story and personality.

DOESN'T DRINK COFFEE

wears these

GRINDS THESE AT NIGHT

HAS BIG TEETH

CUTS HIS OWN HAIR

LIKES TO EAT THIS

WORKS HERE

LIVES HERE

AUSTRALIA

WORRIES A LOT

WEARS THIS

HAS A SISTER & A BROTHER

BORN HERE

SCARED OF PUBLIC SPEAKING

GRANDDAD MADE CHEESE

USES A LOT OF THESE

WEARS THIS

HE HAS DOWN SYNDROME

HAS A QUIFF

LENKA

THEY MADE HIM

QUINN

EATS A LOT OF THIS

MUESLI

SHAVES WITH THIS

SCARED OF THIS

CAN JUGGLE

MARRIED HER

THE DARK

CHECKS LOCKED DOORS

RIDES THIS

HATES TV

HAS MANY SHOES

This illustration is part of *Artists, Writers, Thinkers, Dreamers: Portraits of Fifty Famous Folks and All Their Weird Stuff* to be published by Chronicle Books in 2014.

Heather Diane Hardison

BERKELEY, USA

hdhardison@gmail.com • @illustratedbite
heatherdiane.com • illustratedbites.wordpress.com

" I was born and raised in Eastern North Carolina and studied art and design at North Carolina State University. After graduation in 2009, I moved to the San Francisco Bay Area, where I began working as a sign painter at New Bohemia Signs. I started freelancing in 2010, and in 2012 I starting making a living as a full-time artist.

I am a person of many hobbies (perhaps too many). I'm an avid rock climber, gardener and cooking enthusiast. I'm interested in homesteading, and everything that entails—from making pickles to beekeeping. Most of my illustration assignments are related in some way. It all stems from my illustrated food blog, which was the personal project that launched my freelance career.

Now many of my assignments are more about conveying information than representing an abstract idea. I spend time researching the topic and designing the layout, but not a lot of time conceptualizing, like a lot of editorial illustrators do. I think not having any formal training in illustration has really helped me. I'm not hindered by any preconceived notions of how to be an illustrator, and I think that allows me to be more flexible with my business.

My dream illustration job would involve a combination of hand lettering and illustration, and would be a little heavier on the concept than my usual work. I really enjoy long-form projects, so doing illustrations for a book would be perfect. "

THE ASSIGNMENT

We asked Heather, "If you were to illustrate a portrait of yourself, what would it look like?" She replied, "A bunch of asparagus."

Molly Hatch

NORTHAMPTON, USA

molly@mollyhatch.com • @mollyhatch
mollyhatch.com • mollyhatch.blogspot.com

" I have always been confident in myself to make what I didn't have. I grew up in a family without a lot of resources, but with a lot of raw materials. Craft projects led to making my own clothes, and gardening and homesteading meant we were able to put away food for later. I have always loved art history and coveted the decorative arts. I think a lot of why I make things or design things (or illustrate things) is because I want to have them for myself—I want to see them exist in the world.

I studied drawing, printmaking and ceramics, receiving my BFA at the Museum School in Boston in 2000. After several residencies and apprenticeships in the US and abroad, I received my MFA in ceramics at the University of Colorado in Boulder in 2008. My career has led to collaborations with institutions such as the Museum of Fine Arts in Boston and the Metropolitan Museum of Art in New York. Starting in 2010 through the collaborative development of a line of manufactured home goods carried by Philadelphia-based retailer Anthropologie, I have launched a career as an illustrator, and surface and product designer. My client list has grown exponentially over the last three years to include Anthropologie, Graphique de France, Galison and BHLDN, as well as others.

My start as a studio potter and ceramic artist brings a completely different approach to illustrating and allowed me to find a unique voice.

I work from my home studio in Northampton, Massachusetts, where I live with my husband, daughter and our Border Collie. I have a 350-square-foot garage that we finished off as a studio. It is amazing to have a space that doesn't require a commute, but is also not in my house. When I am in the studio I feel I am not at home; it is really separate. The big benefit is the ability to come and go with things in the studio—I can listen to the baby monitor while my daughter sleeps or naps, and I can work during that time. It's fabulous! "

THE ASSIGNMENT

With a nod to your personal history as a ceramicist, draw something from your ideal day.

{ a GOOD *morning* }

Tea

Cocoa

Espresso

Vicky Healy

BROOKLYN, USA

vickyphealy@gmail.com • @vicky_healy
vickyhealy.com • monsteroclock.wordpress.com

" I don't believe I could have ever chosen a career path that involved me at a desk or had anything to do with math, science, history or computers," muses artist Vicky Healy. "Maybe a park ranger, but only during the daylight."

A fear of the dark doesn't necessarily mean a fear of things that go bump in the night: Vicky adores monsters, or at least the ones that she creates in her imagination. "When I was a young girl I was sitting on my favourite stump in the backyard. I was eating raspberries when I heard something behind me. When I turned around I saw a giant black cat wearing a horse saddle. I dropped my berries and stared open mouthed. He told me that his name was Grumbis and asked me if I wanted to go on a wild adventure. Obviously I said yes."

"My monsters are like my family, I owe them everything, and because of that I would never produce a piece of art with even a speck that is out of place. It is the thing I take most seriously in this world." Her methods are varied: "In terms of illustration I use acrylic on wood panel and sometimes canvas, but when it comes to illustration through sculpture I use rubber molds to make plastic figures."

"I have a studio at home that is great for painting and small sculptures. I think eventually I might need an upgrade but I don't actually like leaving the house, so I would need to win the lottery and buy another apartment in my building."

THE ASSIGNMENT

Monsters aren't always scary; often they're just misunderstood (and hairy) creatures. Why do you feel a kinship with monsters? If you were to represent yourself as a monster, what would it look like?

Sam Hester

CALGARY, CANADA

sam@thedrawingbook.com • @calgaryhester
thedrawingbook.com

THIS PHOTO BY NANC PRICE

" I am all about lines and outlines. Black. I put boxes around everything. I like clear, strong edges and I don't like things to fade out (although sometimes they have to, which is hard for me to handle). All my boxes and black lines probably suggest that I'm a type-A, super-organized, list-making kind of person. That is kind of true.

After I've got my nice strong outlines, I like to use hatching and crosshatching to shade things. I like black-and-white illustrations, but I like colour, too, and when I use colour it's bold and bright. No pastels for me.

My style is inspired by comics, as well as by children's literature. I also like putting text into my pictures. Even if it's not a comics story, there's usually some kind of interjection or commentary that tends to suggest itself.

The better I know something, the better I can draw it. I am really good at drawing myself. Slightly less good at drawing my family and friends. Slightly less good at drawing people I don't know as well. I like drawing people because they are much more interesting to me than anything else (and I can draw people more quickly than I can draw other things, so when time is a factor, people are a good choice).

I also like drawing (and painting) the sky. And I love doing lettering. I have my own lettering style, but any kind appeals. Lettering is probably the most easy, meditative, peaceful, fun kind of 'artwork' for me. "

THE ASSIGNMENT

Document the joys and struggles of being a creative mom.

Judith Hofmann

ENSCHEDE, THE NETHERLANDS

email@judithhofmann.com • @judithhofmann
judithhofmann.com

" I work in a former power transformer building in the Dutch city of Enschede that used to provide a cotton spinning company and the surrounding neighbourhood with electricity. Today the building facilitates an exhibition space for contemporary art and design, and a studio that I share with three other freelancers. Because the exhibitions change about every six weeks I have an ever-changing work environment that I find very inspiring. I also like that I have colleagues with a similar professional background who I can ask for feedback on my work. We like to exchange our experiences with clients and projects during coffee breaks.

I'm inspired by songs, quotes, proverbs and other lingual phenomenons. I make digital collages consisting of lots of different layers and details that I arrange intuitively. I use vintage books, magazines and photographs as source material, as well as some patterned paper, textile or wood structures, so it all adds up to a colourful illustration with a somewhat nostalgic feel. I attempt to make something that people can relate to, that is recognizable but also invites them to look at it from a different perspective—so that it's part of the world as we know it and yet an entrance to a new imaginary world.

When I can take the time off, I love to invite friends over for dinner and cook a special meal for them or make some fancy cake. I find cookbooks very inspiring and would like to make one myself someday, full of family recipes and the stories behind them. "

THE ASSIGNMENT

There is a saying "you are what you eat". Illustrate an imaginary feast of things you like and love. What does it say about you?

Denise Holmes

CHICAGO, USA

hellonisee@gmail.com • @niseemade
niseemade.com

Denise Holmes is inspired by books. "Design books, craft books, children's books, fiction, history, autobiographical books... I am pretty obsessed with books." After years of sitting at a desk job dreaming of illustrating children's books, Denise quit and officially became a freelance illustrator. "I was able to save up enough money to live without a job for a year. I figured if it didn't work out at the end of the year, I would go back to work."

"I was able to earn money selling art prints on Etsy and finding small illustration jobs thanks to Flickr. One day I stumbled upon a website called Aeolidia. I saw they had a bunch of really great illustrators on staff, so I emailed the owner and asked if she would take me on. She did and it helped to launch my career as a freelance illustrator."

"I create original and unique drawings focused on the children's market. I think I have a unique style that makes people happy and is different from other illustrators working in children's books."

With a one-year-old daughter at home, Denise's routine is evolving. "My daughter takes over my day time, which used to be when I would focus on my illustration. I squeeze in emails and research during her naps and draw after she goes to bed for the night. I'm trying to figure out how to balance a life as a mother, wife and illustrator. For now I'm adoring every minute of her during the day and enjoying working in my studio at night."

Denise's dream of illustrating a children's book is coming true. Her first book will be published next year.

THE ASSIGNMENT

Illustrate how you share your love of books with your daughter.

114

Claire Ishino

ADELAIDE, AUSTRALIA

claireishino@gmail.com • claireishino.com
facebook.com/claireishinodesigns

After completing a bachelor of design with a major in jewellery design, Claire Ishino left her native Australia to teach English in Japan. "One year in Japan soon became eight years, during which time I initially taught English conversation and later began making and selling my jewellery. I also met my husband in Japan and we now have two children. We decided to move back to my hometown of Adelaide in 2009, just before the birth of our second baby, and so the next chapter in my life continues here."

Although Claire's illustrations appear simple, they are the result of considerable design and refinement. "They have delicate and intricate elements and show an attention to detail reflective of my background as a jewellery designer. I love using repetitive shapes and textures to create patterns."

"I love drawing plants, leaves and flowers, both real and from my imagination. I love sunny days and changing seasons and inspiring music. I love Japanese paper and tea and origami. I am so inspired by other artists, designers and photographers (including my husband) who are so committed to what they do and achieve excellence in their work. It is truly inspiring to see people doing what they love."

Claire often uses flowers or trees to represent people, and if she were to draw a self-portrait she would do the same with herself. "I think I would draw a simple outline of a flower to represent me, and the inside would be full of pattern for my head and lots of colour for my heart."

THE ASSIGNMENT

Create a colourful pattern design or graphic that contains inspirations from both Australia and Japan.

Emmi Jormalainen

HELSINKI, FINLAND

emmi.jormalainen@gmail.com
emmijormalainen.com

From a studio in Helsinki, Emmi Jormalainen is surrounded by everything she could ever want to draw. "I was dreaming about faraway places with mountains and palm trees when I noticed that if I look closer around me, I can find the most exotic and spectacular things to draw."

"My career has made it possible to have a personal life filled with inspiring things. It's part of my work to look at things more closely: visit museums, zoos, forests and different cities. Life as an illustrator has also pushed me to read more literature in order to learn more about the stories I'm illustrating."

With her trusty pencil, Emmi captures intricate details of scenes both real and imagined, while maintaining a relaxed and whimsical style. "I mostly use just pencil. I like the raw and soft feeling it gives to my pictures. I adore colour, but in the end I enjoy monotone illustrations with soft, dark-grey pencil the most."

She recently self-published a small book documenting all of the places she has lived throughout her life—from her childhood home to small dormitories to a flat she shares with her boyfriend.

Despite this love of home, Emmi chooses to work elsewhere. "I don't work from home. I share a studio with three other creatives. We rented an old fish shop at street level and turned the place into a creative studio. I spend my days drawing there, chatting with friends, eating lunch in the neighbourhood and drinking coffee with random studio guests."

THE ASSIGNMENT

Draw the neighbourhood around your home and studio, showing the character of where you live and work. Add embellishments or imagined stories to enhance the scene.

Patricia Kaegi

SEA CLIFF, USA

theredbowstudio@gmail.com • @pixiewinkle
patriciakaegi.com • redbowstudio.etsy.com

Whether baking brownies or weaving friendship bracelets, Patricia Kaegi was interested in being crafty from an early age. "I have always carried a box of pens and a sketchbook with me everywhere—painting and drawing were a large part of my childhood. I spent much of my free time with a paintbrush, and my favourite babysitters were the ones who knew how to draw."

She didn't realize, however, that art could be a career. "Growing up with two Virgo parents, I never thought of being creative as a career (Virgos are very practical), so I majored in international relations and minored in French." She took many photography and drawing classes on the side. Following graduation (and some time spent skiing and waitressing in Colorado), Patricia studied fashion and textile design at the Academy of Art in San Francisco.

"Then I moved to New York City, working in the fashion industry," she says. "But I was still not satisfied. At that time I began to paint large oils of people. I painted more and more, delving into different types of medium. After having a baby I stopped working in the fashion industry and began teaching after-school art classes to children. I moved out of NYC and opened Red Bow Studio in my town, where I sold my art and taught art classes." With three children now in tow, Patricia closed the physical studio and brought her art practice into her home. "I want to focus whole-heartedly on my art."

"Temporarily I have a home studio so that I can be closer to my newborn daughter. My children enhance my work. You can find my daughters amongst much of my art. They love watching me create and there are many times when they join in."

THE ASSIGNMENT

Illustrate a detailed scene from your day, whether it is at work in your dining room, a scene with your family, picking up the girls from school or riding your bike around town. Give the viewer a sense of place and the joy you feel with these people and locations.

Alistar Khabuliani

ITALY & TBILISI, GEORGIA

contact@alistar.us • @alistar_kh
alistar.us • facebook.com/alistarpage

Alistar Khabuliani has worked on feature films, music videos and advertisements for animation studios in her native Milan, as well as in London and Los Angeles. "After years in animation, I've developed my own style and have started publishing as an illustrator."

Along with this wealth of experience, Alistar brings innate talent and lifelong dedication to her art. She describes herself as a Renaissance woman. "I love to always try something new, to not repeat the same style all my life. My foundation has been in Italy—I've learned from the old masters to be excellent in everything, not just one style. That is the great challenge."

She expresses a will to always be different from what came before, to be in a state of continuous change. "My illustration style can be lively and colourful when I work for children but I can touch darker depths when creating work for adults." The freelance lifestyle suits her perfectly. "It gives me total freedom of movement. I can choose how and where to live. I just need a good internet connection and the rest is simple."

"I live and work now between Italy and Tbilisi, Georgia, an enchanting place where I got married, with my husband and our three children. My work is my life. I don't divide the hours of work and the hours of life; it's all together. I'm able to have intense concentration on a new project and still go to the shop to buy milk or spend the day at the beach with my children."

THE ASSIGNMENT

Illustrate a day at the beach with your children as if it was also a page out of an Italian language book for English-speakers.

My
home
is the
La mia
casa
è il
SEA.
MARE

Sue Jean Ko

NEW YORK CITY, USA

ggosuya@gmail.com • @gosuya
suejeanko.com

"My life has changed dramatically," says Sue Jean Ko. "When I lived in Korea, I kept to myself most of the time. But now I'm studying Illustration in New York City. Living here with great galleries, museums, artists and especially my wonderful school instructors and classmates not only opens my mind but also improves my work." In her native country, Sue Jean has already earned a BFA and MA in digital media design. She worked for a time designing cute textiles for a line of baby products but has enrolled in the illustration program at the School of Visual Arts in New York to focus on her art.

Sue Jean's parents hope she'll return to South Korea after her studies, but they may have to wait a while longer. "I hope to start my illustration career and make a living in New York City," explains Sue Jean. "I don't want to come back empty-handed. I want to succeed. And I really love my family, so I want make them proud of me."

Sue Jean is both intrigued and inspired by American culture. "I love going to food supermarkets, such as Whole Foods Market or Trader Joe's. I can see vivid fruit colours, typography and package design. There are many unusual vegetables that I've never seen before, like artichokes! I also love Michaels arts and crafts store. When I visit, I think, Wow! These Americans never get bored."

THE ASSIGNMENT

From your perspective of being a Korean girl in New York City, create a page of illustrations exemplifying the exuberance of North American consumerism. What things are you attracted to? What items are typically American?

peanut butter
& jelly

Delicious

Danielle Kroll

BROOKLYN, USA

danielleleekroll@gmail.com
hellodaniellekroll.com

anielle Kroll won her fifth grade's Enthusiastic Artist Award, which provided a summer's worth of painting classes. "My teacher was a kooky old lady who kept a family of geese as pets by her studio, which overlooked a pretty lake." Growing up in what she describes as "the best part of New Jersey," Danielle had a treehouse, playgrounds and forests that encouraged play and adventure.

After studying graphic design at the Tyler School of Art, she worked in Anthropologie's Philadelphia-based art department for three years. "Eventually I felt that I needed a change of scenery, so I left Philly to pursue a freelance illustration and design career in Brooklyn."

With gouache as her preferred medium, Danielle's quirky and playful style turns everyday things into something special. "I like to draw ordinary items like lamps, furniture, shoes and glassware. I'm always doodling patterns, too." She adores vintage objects. "I'm very sentimental," she says. "If I were to draw a self-portrait it would probably involve some of my favourite things from my childhood. I used to have a junk drawer filled with my most precious little toys, like a mouse sitting on a piece of cheese, a Chinese throwing star and my sticker collection."

If you were to spy on Danielle while she was working, you'd most likely find her on the floor, surrounded by books with loose leaf papers scattered about. "I make a big mess. I actually like to paint on the floor. It's more relaxing than sitting upright at a desk."

THE ASSIGNMENT

Draw objects from your childhood paired with items from your life now. How are things the same? What is different?

my favorite things

MY OLD
NIGHTLIGHT

FROM MY FIRST
JEWELRY BOX

CERAMIC
ROOSTER HEAD FROM
GRANDMA JOE'S KITCHEN

Luscious

BEST MUG FOR TEA

FOUND THIS IN GRANDMA'S BASEMENT

USED TO
LIVE IN THE
ATTIC OF MY
DOLLHOUSE

Gabriela Larios

LONDON, UK

creativestudio@gabrielalarios.com • @GabrielaLarios1
gabrielalarios.com • gabotelarios.blogspot.co.uk

Gabriela Larios is originally from El Salvador, where she worked as a designer. In 2006 she was awarded a scholarship to undertake a master of arts at the London-based Camberwell College of Arts. "It was something I had always dreamed of," she says. "Moving to a new country was definitely a life-changing experience. While living in London I met my other half, and when I finished my MA my husband was offered a very good job in London and we decided to establish ourselves and our little family here. Since then, alongside becoming a mum for the first time, I continued focusing on creating a solid style and growing as an artist."

Her illustration style is cheerful and fun, with influences from her culture. "I believe that style is the result of each person's life experiences and interests, and therefore I do believe my art has been strongly influenced by my Latin American roots and elements from European culture."

"For me there is no better feeling than enjoying the creative process and being amazed by the results you get as you refine your craft." Gabriela continues to hone her skills from a corner of her home. "There is a big window with lots of light coming through that cheers up the atmosphere when the days are grey and cold."

When the days are nice, Gabriela heads outdoors to explore London by bike. "I love cycling. I used to take part in El Salvador's female triathlon and the road cycling team, but cycling especially is a sport close to my heart. If I were not an illustrator I think I would have dedicated myself to becoming a professional cyclist. Nowadays my bike is my car."

THE ASSIGNMENT

Inspired by your love of cycling, create a textile pattern suitable for your toddler daughter's bedroom.

Kelly Lasserre

NEW YORK CITY, USA

kellylasserre@gmail.com
kellylasserre.com • kellylasserre.tumblr.com

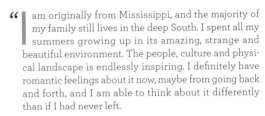

" I am originally from Mississippi, and the majority of my family still lives in the deep South. I spent all my summers growing up in its amazing, strange and beautiful environment. The people, culture and physical landscape is endlessly inspiring. I definitely have romantic feelings about it now, maybe from going back and forth, and I am able to think about it differently than if I had never left.

I grew up most of my life, including my school years, on the south shore of Massachusetts in a small Irish fishing town, very different from Mississippi, but also kind of dreamy—just not as interesting. But I feel very fortunate being from two completely opposite parts of the country; it has made me feel very balanced in a way.

In my teenage years I had a real desire to make things and to communicate visually—it just made each day simpler. At some point I realized it was more than an angsty teenage need to express myself, so I really pushed my interest and had a lot of support from some great teachers. I went to art school at the Maryland Institute College of Art where I graduated with a BFA in illustration in 2008.

My style has been pared down over the years into something that is very simple, intentional, concise. I used to be more self-conscious about my style because it didn't have this traditional approach to telling stories that fit into the illustration work I was being exposed to. But I eventually just let myself do what came naturally, which happens to be very direct and to the point.

Currently I am living and working in New York City. It's not the easiest place to live, but it is very stimulating, frustrating, endlessly entertaining and inspiring. I've had to be very patient to make it work so far. But I just moved to Queens so I could afford to live in this absurd city yet also have enough space to work and breathe a bit. And I now have a studio, which is ideal. "

THE ASSIGNMENT

Select a grouping of everyday objects from your home that tell the viewer a little something about you. Through observation and your illustration skills elevate the items into something beautiful.

tony chachere's
on everything
all the time

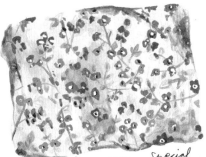

dreamy
pillow + special
ancient
pillow case

french press
&
favorite mug

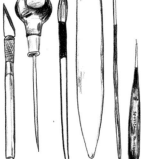

tools
for
making

handy message cross-stitched
by my mama decades ago

A task is
of it as fun   quickly done
if you think!

shoe shine stool
(bedside table)

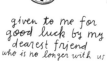

given to me for
good luck by my
dearest friend
who is no longer with us

old railroad nail spike
with john henry painted
on it in white

JOHN HENRY

Christina Leist

VANCOUVER, CANADA

chris@christinaleist.com
christinaleist.com

After some years in Frankfurt's advertising industry, Christina Leist paid a visit to Canada's west coast. "I decided to stay and enjoy its inspiring beauty and the space that it offers for a little longer than planned. I had found people in the city that wanted to work with me as an illustrator. I thought that this was a good sign, and stayed. Years later, I am still here, surrounded by ocean and trees. Vancouver is my home base, but I visit Germany several times a year."

Now a successful children's book illustrator, Christina's style is cheerful and playful. "I try to keep a positive view of the world and to stay light-hearted. I think my illustrations express this clearly," she says. This positive attitude is also expressed through her yoga practise and connection to nature. "I like to be outside in nature, moving my body. Horses have also been a big part of my life, although during the last years it has been a long-distance relationship—my horse is still in Germany. He is 29 and retired."

In Vancouver, her home is her studio—and vice versa. "The illustrator's life is always present or partially tucked into the many drawers and closets of my space. The benefit of it being this way is that I can enjoy an amazing ocean view and view of the neighbourhood all day long. I am inside, but I feel connected."

THE ASSIGNMENT

Tell a story about your long-distance relationship with your horse in Germany. Christina describes, "My contribution is showing what would happen if Kalle (my senior, 29-year-old horse) was surprising me with his visit—or even his immigration."

Avital Manor

TEL AVIV, ISRAEL

avitalmanor@gmail.com
avitalmanor.com • blog.avitalmanor.com

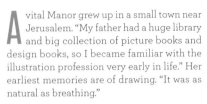

Avital Manor grew up in a small town near Jerusalem. "My father had a huge library and big collection of picture books and design books, so I became familiar with the illustration profession very early in life." Her earliest memories are of drawing. "It was as natural as breathing."

The path to becoming an illustrator had a few detours. "After a traumatic service in the army—which is, unfortunately, mandatory where I live—it was really hard for me to draw, so I decided to major in my second-best field: math." With a degree in mathematics and computer science, she worked as a software developer for several years. In 2007 she went back to school, this time for a formal education in illustration and design. "I was lucky enough to find a very supportive spouse who encouraged me to not let go of my dreams."

"My studio is at home and my spouse is a designer, too, so we have this new arrangement: once a week I get the whole day to myself, without taking care of home tasks, and the same goes for him. The rest of the week from 4 pm, when our kid comes back from nursery school, we spend the time together (unless one of us has a deadline . . .)."

"I think starting late—this is my second career—and having a child in this early stage of the career naturally slows down my pace, but there are advantages: I get a lot of inspiration and perspective from my kid, I have my family support and I have more artistic collaborations."

THE ASSIGNMENT

Draw and document where you live in Tel Aviv—the community, your home or your studio. Would you look at the broad view or dive into the details?

AVITAL MANOR

Michael Mateyko

CALGARY, CANADA

mm@komboh.com
komboh.com

" I spend too much time watching terrible films with my friends," admits Michael Mateyko. "It started out as a joke, but as time progressed it's become a horrible and comforting ritual. I'm not sure if it's been very beneficial."

Michael had a "nerdy" childhood, was once an engineering student and didn't draw a thing in his life until he applied to art school. "I made a run at art school to see if I could learn a little about how to make pictures. I met a wonderful group of people who shared the same passions as me, and I was finally home." Since graduating from the Alberta College of Art + Design in Calgary in 2009, Michael has been working freelance and in agencies doing advertising, design and illustration.

If he wasn't an illustrator, Michael's alternate professions (in ascending order of probability) would be: tour guide at Jurassic Park, astronaut, visual effects worker, cartographer or software engineer. Viewers can see hints of all of those pursuits in Michael's illustrations, which are characteristically geometric, clean, bold and even "antiseptic," as Michael himself describes them. "There's a general anal-retentiveness, detail-obsession and rigidity to my work—but on the flip-side, a sense of playfulness and humour within those constraints."

"My dream assignment would be producing posters and covers for Criterion. Or doing in-world graphic design and poster design for Pixar. Or getting a piece in *Wired* or *Monocle*."

THE ASSIGNMENT

Acknowledging your hobby of watching terrible films with friends, create a movie poster about one of your favourites, belying the terribleness of the film with your skills as an illustrator and designer.

THE LOVE GURU

DEMANDS
LAUGHTER

Amyisla Mccombie

LONDON, UK

*amyislamccombie@hotmail.co.uk • @amyislamccombie
cargocollective.com/amyisla • amyisla.tumblr.com*

Amyisla Mccombie was brought up in the land of Shakespeare, in Stratford-upon-Avon. A fresh graduate of illustration, Amyisla is just starting her professional life in London.

"The best thing about being an illustrator is that I get to draw and play with paint every day," she says. "What else can be better? Being creative and just doing what you love is pretty great. As is the idea that you're inspiring others' imaginations. You can help create amazing images. The worst thing is the loneliness—it is not the most interactive of jobs, unless you're in a shared studio. When you reach an artist block, that can be hard, but it's nothing that a good gallery and coffee can't solve."

For Amyisla, work and life blend. "I never have a day where I don't do a bit of illustration, whether that's writing down ideas or spending the day painting. I think that being an illustrator isn't so much a job—I think it's sort of a lifestyle."

"I loved creating images and pieces of work based on fairy tales and narratives, so I decided that I would study illustration. Sometimes I love to create work that is from my own interests, but I also love briefs given to me. I love a challenge and think it's important to test yourself, and this only improves your work. I also enjoy it because you learn about areas that you wouldn't have known about before. Other people's ideas are so exciting, and it's amazing to be able to illustrate them!"

THE ASSIGNMENT

Go for a day of sightseeing in your city—visit galleries, museums, shops and/or cafés. Create an illustration of the highlights, incorporating some hand lettering or personal commentary. Imagine this as an assignment for a guide book or travel feature in a magazine.

BIG BEN

KEW Garden's

ST Paul's Cathedral

LONDON EYE

Donna McKenzie

CHARLOTTE, USA

corelladesign@att.net • @corelladesign
donnamckenzieillustration.com • corelladesign.etsy.com

"My father was an artist, art teacher and graphic designer who was always inviting me to be his assistant. My mother, being an avid gardener, gave me her love of nature. I have always loved making, drawing and dancing—growing up, my heart was always in dance. In college, I studied psychology first and computer science second. With psychology I hoped to become a dance therapist. And with computer science I landed the corporate job with benefits that my father wanted for me. While working at that corporate job I met my husband. After having two children, I began rethinking what I really wanted to do with my life and began making and creating again.

I began painting furniture, knitting and drawing for friends. Opening an Etsy shop was my first venture into the world of selling my work. When I began to get requests for custom work I thought: this is something that I really, really want to do. As I move forward in my career, I remember so many things that I used to do growing up—making jewelry, working in the dark room, working for my father's graphic design business. These things felt natural to me. Working in a cubicle did not.

I definitely lean more toward drawing people or animals. I am interested in living creatures and how they think and react. I usually work with black and white and a little colour. I think I have a lot of opposites going on in my personality. I can be very outgoing sometimes, and then other times quite shy.

Now I want to do so many things with my work. I would love to illustrate children's books, album covers and book jacket designs, as well as children's textiles or decor. "

THE ASSIGNMENT

The classic assignment with a few additions: if you were an animal, what animal would you be? What would you be wearing? What textile or wallpaper pattern would be behind you?

Dinara Mirtalipova

SAGAMORE HILLS, USA

hello@mirdinara.com • @mirdinara
mirdinara.com • mirdinara.blogspot.com

Once upon a time, there was a little Uzbek girl who believed in fairy tales. She moved to the United States and her wishes came true: she became an artist. Dinara Mirtalipova is an artist who was raised on folklore and who is still very much drawn to the beauty of folk songs, stories and art.

"I never believed I could turn my passion into my profession. I studied cybernetics in college and always thought that art was just my hobby. But boy was I wrong. With time I understood that all I wanted to do in life was draw made-up stories and illustrate what was in my head. And it was never quiet in my head. So in the beginning I started a blog where I uploaded my doodles. But with time my blog expanded and people started responding to my illustrations, leaving positive comments and even asking me to draw for them. I knew it was time to start a new career."

"If I weren't an illustrator, I would definitely be a sailor. I would sail the seven seas and I would curse like a sailor. I think I would never settle down and would be travelling and spending all the money I had in my pocket. And I would stay up all night and dance 'til I dropped." The beauty of being an illustrator is that you can live in those alternate realities through your work. Dinara agrees. "I think all illustrators are free-minded people, people who see the world from a unique perspective. They all live in their own made-up worlds—the worlds of imagination."

In Dinara's real world, she is a mom to a young child. "As soon as I got to hold my daughter for the first time I knew I had changed. She changed me not only on an emotional level; she turned everything at our house upside down. It took me a good two years to re-adjust to my new role and to the way I work."

THE ASSIGNMENT

Create a pattern inspired by the natural world.

Sandra Monat

SIEGBURG, GERMANY

sandra@herzensart.com • @herzensart
herzensart.com • herzensart.blogspot.com

After eight years at a software company with her free time spent painting, Sandra Monat noticed that the gap between her job and her vision of leading a creative life was growing bigger. Feeling the stress of not being authentic to her creative self, Sandra quit her job and declared that she would be a full-time artist.

From her home in Germany, Sandra developed her craft of designing and sewing textile art toys under the moniker Herzensart. Vikings, cowboys and other fellows make up the cast of quirky characters that she sells through her online shop. "Cutting fabrics led me to cutting paper. Soon I began to transform my textile dolls into paper dolls, which I used for illustrating several items, like stationery, fabrics and gifts."

"My figures are handcut and the papers I'm using are often found or recycled from packaging material, magazines, books, etc. I try to use the least amount of computer editing as possible to keep the handmade look."

Ten years on, Sandra still enjoys creating characters and their little worlds. "Being allowed to play and work with beautiful material, like fabric and paper, that's what I really love to do." She looks forward to expanding her creative reach through other partnerships. "My experience with assignments is still young, but very positive. Since I really love to see my work on different mediums, I plan to focus on more collaborations in the future."

THE ASSIGNMENT

Take your characters on a seafaring adventure.

Ilichna Morasky

MONTREAL, CANADA

imorasky@gmail.com
strangerfamiliar.com

" I was born with my finger attached to my face, leaving a pretty cool scar next to my right eye. It is possibly the reason my vivid imagination communicates so regularly with my right hand. Since their fateful separation, beauty stirring with unease and dark humour enters my work through a haze of acrylic, detailed linework and wood grain.

What I find so powerful about illustration is how it stimulates a clear thought and emotion while transcending reality. Imagine in your day-to-day seeing a beautiful face chomping down on a large dragonfly or someone blowing butterflies like bubbles out of their mouth. These things that should be impossible can be seen and felt through the power of drawing. In the process of making, you transcend reality, melting away the hours while you jump from corner to corner in your imagination. In my particular process, I've found a way to marry my love of drawing and painting using photocopy transfers and acrylic on wood.

Most weekends I'll go to a local café where there's live music at all hours and just draw the musicians and their unique toys. I would be over the moon if I could illustrate a book or anthology, start to finish—something written by a musician I admire. I often look at Radiohead's *In Rainbows* vinyl box set or Beck's sheet music and think how fun it would be to collaborate on a project like that. Also any chance to have my work displayed in film would incredible.

However, despite the love of creating, I have—more than once—turned down/pretended not to hear my mom's plea for me to produce some Anne Geddes-style paintings of babies for her walls. Call it pride or boredom, but I just can't bring myself to do it. But that's mostly just an anecdote about being a bad daughter. "

THE ASSIGNMENT

Illustrate your favourite song, with yourself as a character within it.

Favourite song: "I only have eyes for you"

Helen Musselwhite

MANCHESTER, UK

hello@helenmusselwhite.com • @paperhelen
helenmusselwhite.com • instagram.com/helenmusselwhite

Helen Musselwhite lives on the southern edge of Manchester, with one foot in suburbia and another in the English countryside. It's a location that inspires with its beauty and its history of craftsmanship: "the skill of artists and craftsmen from the past who didn't have the technology, tools and ease of life we have today but still managed to produce amazing and beautiful work that's lasted and is still relevant today." This ethos pushes her to perfect her skills. "My work is very analogue and the finished product is a physical thing rather than a file on a computer. I work very hard to make it perfect both on a visual and a crafted level." This process requires time and concentration. "I don't have children and quite frankly I don't think I'd be able to work at this level if I did!"

Using a layered, cut-paper technique, Helen uses a scalpel or small embroidery scissors to cut out each paper piece. "I score, fold and curl where needed and then build up the layers with foam board. I photograph each stage and keep in touch with my art director as I make a piece so changes can be made if necessary. When everyone is happy I glue everything into place and take photos of the finished piece for my archive. Usually the art director arranges for photography, so I make foam board boxes for the artwork and send."

"I work alone from a studio in my house and I do sometimes spill out into other rooms and I frequently leave a trail of paper offcuts around the house. I do like working from home as it means I can be flexible, but I do think it would be good to be with like-minded people sometimes, as working alone can be insular. I love going on photo shoots for this reason but I always think I chat too much whilst on them!"

When taking a break from work, Helen enjoys taking her dog for a walk. "Taking him for daily walks means I get away from the studio and I get to see the countryside and see the seasons change, which inspires my work."

THE ASSIGNMENT

Go for a walk with your dog in the English countryside and construct a paper illustration inspired by the experience. Envision the resulting illustration as a still from an animated film or a page from an illustrated book.

Ed Nacional

BROOKLYN, USA

ed@ednacional.com • @ednacional
ednacional.com

" I grew up in the standard suburban life playing Lego and doodling the days away. My dad worked as an architect and we never had a shortage of paper and pencils around. There were drafting tables, rulers, Letraset, electric erasers and all the other tools to design by hand. He could write the alphabet perfectly and precisely with ease. Not only was his work creative he also had hobbies in photography and computers.

My mom was also hands-on and creative. She made our cakes and decorated them with full scenes using our favourite toys and characters, and she crocheted all our mittens, hats and blankets. My parents pushed this culture of DIY and creating things for both fun and function. Growing up in this world of making brought me to where I am today. I studied graphic design and more recently started illustration, but I attribute that willingness to explore new worlds to my parents.

The things that inspire me for my work are the same things that inspire me in life. Travelling, going to museums and scrounging thrift stores, antique malls and flea markets all fuel my work. People say the thing you do in your spare time is the thing you should be doing for a living. I feel lucky to have that.

My love for vintage products and design fuels my career and informs the things I make. My wife and I have a dream to further incorporate these things into our lives. If I can balance a design and illustration career as well as find and sell vintage housewares, that would be amazing. We would love to push that idea even further and start making our own housewares. "

THE ASSIGNMENT

Inspired by your love of '50-'70s design and craft, create an illustration or series of icons that would be used in a guidebook for vintage collectors. The guidebook would be sold in the vintage furniture shop owned by you and your wife.

Jenny Nieh

PHILADELPHIA, USA

jennynieh@gmail.com
jennynieh.com

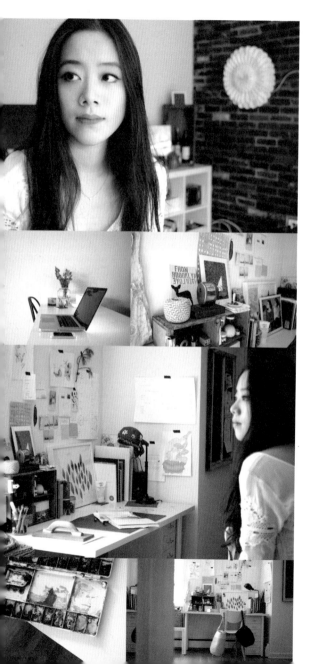

J enny Nieh spent her formative years in Taiwan, Singapore and China. "I'm a third-culture kid who grew up with languages and influences that constantly made me crave for a world without boundaries. In my mind I am a constant traveller, aware of but unaffected by cultural norms. For me, travelling is a never-ending experience instead of something with a destination. This allows me to constantly strive to cherish moments and connections with the world around me and to live the concept that our lives are filled with cycles that continue to teach us something new (or old) for the rest of our lives."

Jenny became an artist because she wanted to see the world and document it in her own unique way. "To be able to experience and capture colours, moments, patterns and all the details, rearrange them into how I as an artist believe they ought to be represented, and create a new world that belongs to me and yet can be shared with everyone else—that is what I love and why I wanted to be an artist."

"I moved to Brooklyn to study art the Pratt Institute. It was the best experience anyone could have as an aspiring artist and traveller." She and her husband currently live in Philly. "Relocation has always been a big part of my life, and will continue to be."

In a fluid, quiet style, Jenny's watercolours are evocative of places and feelings. "I value illustrating as an experience, an emotion, and I am open to illustration as an ambiguous or abstract term. I believe in the emotion that is put into the details of the work to form something that can be unexpected and successful."

THE ASSIGNMENT

Imagine your family is taking a drive through your favourite place in the world. Draw the impression of what you'd see out the window of the passenger's seat.

Shaw Nielsen

DENVER, USA

shaw@shawnielsen.com • @shawnielsen
shawnielsen.com • blog.shawnielsen.com

"I was born in Denver, Colorado—pencil in hand," shares Shaw Nielsen. "For as long as I can remember I've had an overactive imagination and a passion for doodling, so you could say I've always been on a collision course with a career as an illustrator."

"I always start off a project with oodles of doodling. It's my favourite part of any project because the options are just so infinite at this point. So a sketchbook is always at the heart of my process. I burn through two or three of them in a month. I usually jump to the computer once I've settled on an idea and just start with a blank art board in Adobe Illustrator, referencing my sketch as I draw with my mouse. Next I'll take my vector art into Adobe Photoshop and apply textures and tweak the illustration a bit to really bring the piece to life."

Shaw says that a good dose of play is integral to his creative process. "Taking a step back to drink a cold beer or to play fetch with my pup is as much a part of my process as my pencil or computer. I just don't think I could do the work I do without being happy and grounded by reminders of why I love living."

With an enviable client list including *The New York Times, Reader's Digest, HOW* magazine and the *Wall Street Journal*, Shaw has set his sites beyond North America. "I've been at this for long enough that I've worked with most folks I'd like to, though I'd love to work with more international clients. Illustration can span culture and language, and that is something I love tackling."

THE ASSIGNMENT

You stated that if you weren't an illustrator, you'd be a panda tamer. Draw this!

Elizabeth Olwen

TORONTO, CANADA

hello@elizabetholwen.com • @elizabetholwen
elizabetholwen.com

" My mother moved to Canada from Ireland and met my dad, who was an automotive painter and the artist behind many hot babe van murals. I entered the world during a time when the greatest entertainment for kids was in making their own fun—building couch forts, finding a giant cardboard box in the bin and turning it into a dream home and doodling on lined Hilroy paper with blue ballpoint pens.

I loved my arts and crafts, and stayed the course all the way through to art school, where I discovered graphic design and fell in love. I worked for years at design agencies where the goal was to create for corporate clients before I realized that something was missing, at which point I quit my job, went to Berlin for three months and rediscovered the desire to create. I came home from Berlin with a hefty portfolio of patterns, a creative spark and sense of fulfillment that I hadn't felt in years. A few years later, my patterns are starting to find themselves onto products across the globe and I'm thrilled.

As a child, I was obsessed with patterns. I was mesmerized by the orange floral drapes in my mother's kitchen. Surrounded by bold, unapologetic prints, patterns were something that I could lose myself in; a window to faraway places. Through the years, the love of patterns remained and crept its way into my DNA. I would see beautiful wallpapers and my heart would ache a little and it eventually pushed me to wholeheartedly pursue my art. "

THE ASSIGNMENT

Your portfolio of surface design is categorized with themes such as "1950s Florals", "Retro Morocco" and "Festive Forest". Using your love of baking as inspiration, create a new theme called "Home Sweet Home".

HOME
sweet
HOME

Clare Owen

BRISTOL, UK

clare@clareowen.co.uk • @ukeladyclare
clareowen.co.uk

GOOD
THINGS
ARE TO
COME

Clare Owen draws like a girl. And this is a very good thing. Soft colour palettes and a quirky, handwritten script feature in some of her past client work. She has created stationery for Galison and prints for Urban Outfitters, and has illustrated books—notably a ladies' guide to riding and owning a bicycle.

"I suppose I am quite feminine without necessarily being too girly, and perhaps that's apparent in my illustration. I am also a massive francophile, which also pops up." The illustration market loves a style like Clare's: approachable, sweet and interesting. "My illustrations are contemporary but still quite accessible and feminine. So they feel fresh without being too 'out there'."

"I've tried to create a body of work that celebrates femininity. I am definitely a feminist. Not in a man-hating way, just a 'if a macaroon makes you excited, that's okay' kind of way."

Speaking of macaroons, Clare's favourite thing to draw is food. "I want to be on Marks and Spencer's food packaging," she says. "I love the combination of illustration and design they use in their food hall and would love to see some of my work in there."

Clare was born and raised in the South West of England, and graduated from Plymouth University with a First Class Honours in illustration in 2009. She lives in Bristol and plans to return to school to pursue a master's degree.

THE ASSIGNMENT

Drawing upon your love of food and inspired by recent travel to France, illustrate the foods and/or packages of your ideal French feast.

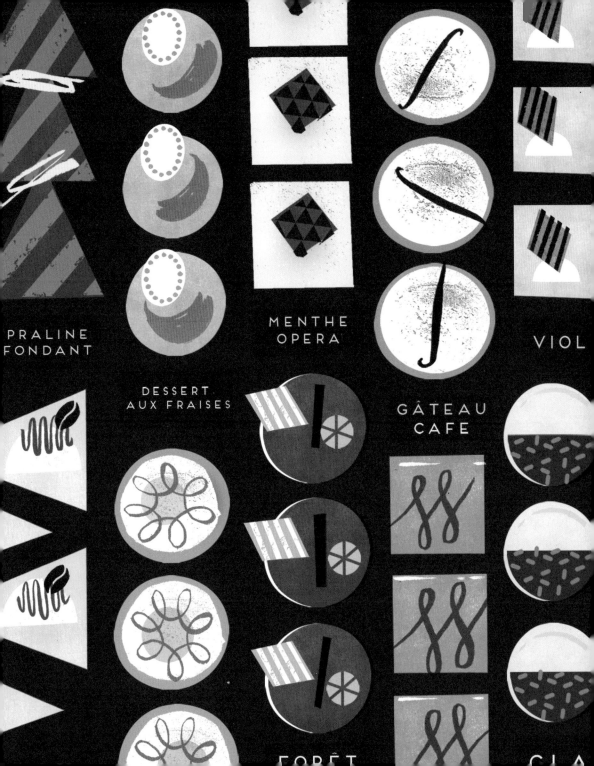

PRALINE
FONDANT

MENTHE
OPERA

VIOL

DESSERT
AUX FRAISES

GÂTEAU
CAFE

FORÊT

CLA

Cleo Papanikolas

BERKELEY, USA

cleo@cleomade.com
cleomade.com

An illustrator's first published drawing is a right of passage. "One of my first solo, moment-to-shine magazine assignments was to draw a latke—a flat, brown, shredded pile." It might have been a challenge, but for Cleo Papanikolas, drawing food is a passion. She authored the book *Cook Until Desired Tenderness*, a sort of graphic novel of five visual essays. Her magical realism approach to illustration is achieved with gouache, pencil, acrylic, ink and perhaps a little Photoshop. She has an appreciation for detail but knows when to stop before overworking a piece.

Cleo enjoys a spacious studio built in the backyard of the Berkeley home she shares with her husband and two boys. "Living arrangements are always driven by studio space. In school, I slept in a tiny attic space so I could use the bedroom as a studio. When we bought our house, we chose a tiny house on a big lot, with room to build a studio. I choose to live compactly in order to have a big, open, airy space for art."

Cleo describes her balance of work and life half-jokingly: "When the boys are at school it's all about me; when they are home I'm doing stuff for them. And then there are the days when they are home and I have an assignment—so I turn on the TV, find old Halloween candy and throw a huge bomb of it all over the room, let them take all the Kleenex out of a box and tape everything in the house together with masking tape, while I try to disappear into my computer. And then I pay for it later."

THE ASSIGNMENT

Share some personal artifacts: open your handbag, a desk drawer, the fridge or a kitchen cabinet and document what you see. What does it say about you?

160

Sun Young Park

NEW YORK, USA

hello@sunyoungpark.co • @talktospark
sunyoungpark.co

"Drawing, painting and observing the world around me in search of art in happenstance has always been my quiet, personal and happy place. I spend more time doing this than I'd like to admit." Some may call this procrastination; others may call it meditation. For Sun Young Park, it was a clue to what she should do with her life. "I guess that's what makes me an artist. Becoming an illustrator seemed a natural solution to what my professional direction should be."

Sun has illustrated a number of popular non-fiction books for publishers such as Melanie Falick/STC Craft (an imprint of Abrams) and Artisan. "I truly enjoyed drawing animals and vegetables attempting to escape their impending doom at the hands of chef April Bloomfield for her cookbook *A Girl and Her Pig*." With ink lines and watercolours combined with vector graphics and Photoshop finishes, Sun's style is playful and fresh.

Despite her impressive portfolio, Sun shares the doubts common to most illustrators. "The worst thing about being an illustrator is the challenge of illustrating a client's vision while not compromising my own. Coming up with a solution and style that makes both the client and myself happy and proud takes a lot of sketching and conversation."

Conversely, the best thing about being an illustrator is the chance for exploration, discovery and personal development. "I like that I have a job where I get to change things up constantly. No two works have to be the same, nor should they be. I get to materialize a concept the best way possible with whatever technique that may be, and I don't have to be pigeon-holed into one particular style."

Newly married, Sun lives in New York with her husband. "We're seriously considering adopting a dog."

THE ASSIGNMENT

Draw a scene from your life as a newlywed illustrator.

Meera Lee Patel

JERSEY CITY, USA

meera.lee.patel@gmail.com • @meeralee
meeralee.com • yaymeeralee.etsy.com

Meera Lee Patel has only been illustrating for a short while. Two years ago, she graduated from college and secured a job with a publishing company. "I edited papers and put my knowledge of the *Oxford Style Manual* to good use." She has always been interested the publishing industry. "I enjoy writing and literature to a very intense degree—it's what fuels most of my illustration and propels me to tell stories with my work."

However, the desk job wasn't for her. "It was only a few months before I knew I'd slowly go insane if I didn't make a drastic change. With a slew of pent-up creative energy and strong desire for self-sufficiency, I opened up an Etsy shop, started to take commissioned illustration jobs and began, once again, to let my imagination guide me."

The transition from words to pictures was natural. "I grew up telling stories with my words; eventually I learned to tell them silently, with scribbles, colour and feeling. I'd always been a creative soul, writing and illustrating my own short stories and novels from a young age, using my imagination as fuel to create my own happiness."

"My work is very bright, spirited and detailed. I work very small—inspired by the miniature paintings of my native India—and add extremely tiny details to every portion of the piece. I would love to illustrate and write a strange and magical children's book. I've already written and illustrated two of my own, but it would be very fulfilling to do so with a reputable publishing company who believes in me and my work."

THE ASSIGNMENT

You wrote, "In a past life, I was a baby mastodon with floral-patterned tusks." Please draw this magical creature. How did it get its floral tusks?

Ashley Percival

CORNWALL, UK

*ashleypercival@hotmail.co.uk • @ashleypercival_*
AshleyPercival.etsy.com

Bespectacled owls, cycling ungulates and skateboarding sloths all adorned in colourfully patterned knitwear, scarves and toques make up the cast of characters in Ashley Percival's popular Etsy shop.

"After graduating, a friend advised me to create a Tumblr blog to show off my illustrations. I decided to give it a go and began to upload new illustrations every day. I soon started to gain followers and received lots of nice comments about my work. I found out about Etsy and decided to try to sell art prints, and sold six prints on my first day. This was amazing as I have always wanted to be an illustrator and sell my artwork." With 1,600 sales and counting, Ashley's first years as a freelancer have been exciting. He recently enjoyed having a display of his work in the London tube.

"I grew up in a beautiful coastal place called Cornwall in England. I spent most of my childhood on the beach, skateboarding and drawing. If I illustrated myself I would be dressed in a similar way as my animal characters. I would be wearing a hat, jeans, shirt or jumper and have a skateboard."

"I prefer to create work using my own ideas," he says. "I love creating unique art prints and clothing designs, and soon hope to illustrate my own children's books."

THE ASSIGNMENT

Draw an anthropomorphic portrait of yourself on a skateboard, giving clues to your personality and style.

Mary Peterson

LOS ANGELES, USA

*mary@marypeterson.com • marypeterson.com
letterpresshabitat.etsy.com*

Mary Peterson grew up on a picture-book family farm in Iowa. "We grew corn and beans, and raised cows, pigs, sheep and chickens. We had horses for work and pleasure, a dog (actually a series of dogs, all named Tippy) and oodles of barn cats," she recalls fondly. "I married young and had a baby so it made perfect sense to move to California. Some ups and downs were had and it was back to Iowa, where I eventually went to college and studied art. Then I moved back to California for good. Ever since, I've been happily working away as an artist, graphic designer, illustrator, mother and wife." The creative lifestyle is a positive influence on her family. "We live simply and within our means and are happy to do so. No regrets. No time wasted."

Mary's dream is to create a book for toddlers or preschoolers using her letterpress and lino block printing techniques. Already a successful children's book illustrator with half a dozen titles in another style, Mary has yet to explore the possibilities of her linocut method for a narrative story. "I aim to bring humour and comfort through a simple narrative."

In her printmaking technique, one can appreciate the physical effort required to produce an image and can see Mary's love of old advertising art in the resulting prints. The flat colours reference an older age of children's books, where a simple number of coloured inks were overprinted and registered (and misregistered) with charming results.

THE ASSIGNMENT

Using your letterpress or linoleum technique: make an illustration of the "picture-book" family farm of your childhood, as it would be used in a book for preschoolers, with Tippy as the main character.

Susy Pilgrim Waters

BOSTON, USA & UK

pilgrimwaters@me.com
pilgrimwaters.com • pilgrimwaters.co

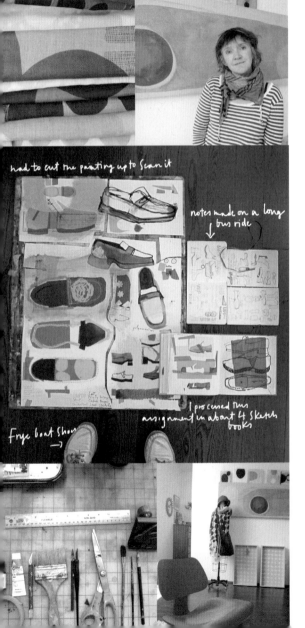

had to cut the painting up to scan it

notes made on a long
bus ride
↓

I processed this
assignment in about 4 sketch
books

Frye boat shoes
→

" I have an inner drive and, frankly, a need to be an illustrator," explains Susy Pilgrim Waters. "I love making functional and practical items and art." Describing herself as practical and realistic and "compulsively decorative," Susy's creativity is in her blood. "I am compelled to tell stories and make pages and objects look good."

Susy's work has been widely published, and she has worked with such clients as Crate & Barrel, Chronicle Books, the New York Public Library and Target. Her work is truly multimedia: she uses acrylic, watercolours, inks and more, incorporated with elements of both physical and digital collage. This complex and layered style is colourful, energetic and very expressive.

Susy finds inspiration everywhere and enjoys hobbies such as knitting, woodblock printing and bike riding. "I love to window shop occasionally and visit really cool stores. To see really well-made shoes or clothes is fascinating to me. Well-crafted and handmade items always please me. I think it relates to my personal standards—though not to my purse!"

She recently expanded her creative offerings by designing a line of scarves. Featuring bold graphics in earthy tones, the Merino wool scarves are individually handwoven and hand silk-screened in Kathmandu, Nepal.

THE ASSIGNMENT

"I would LOVE to design and make shoes, too."

Illustrate a Pilgrim Waters line of shoes. Are they practical or fantastical? Or a little bit of both?

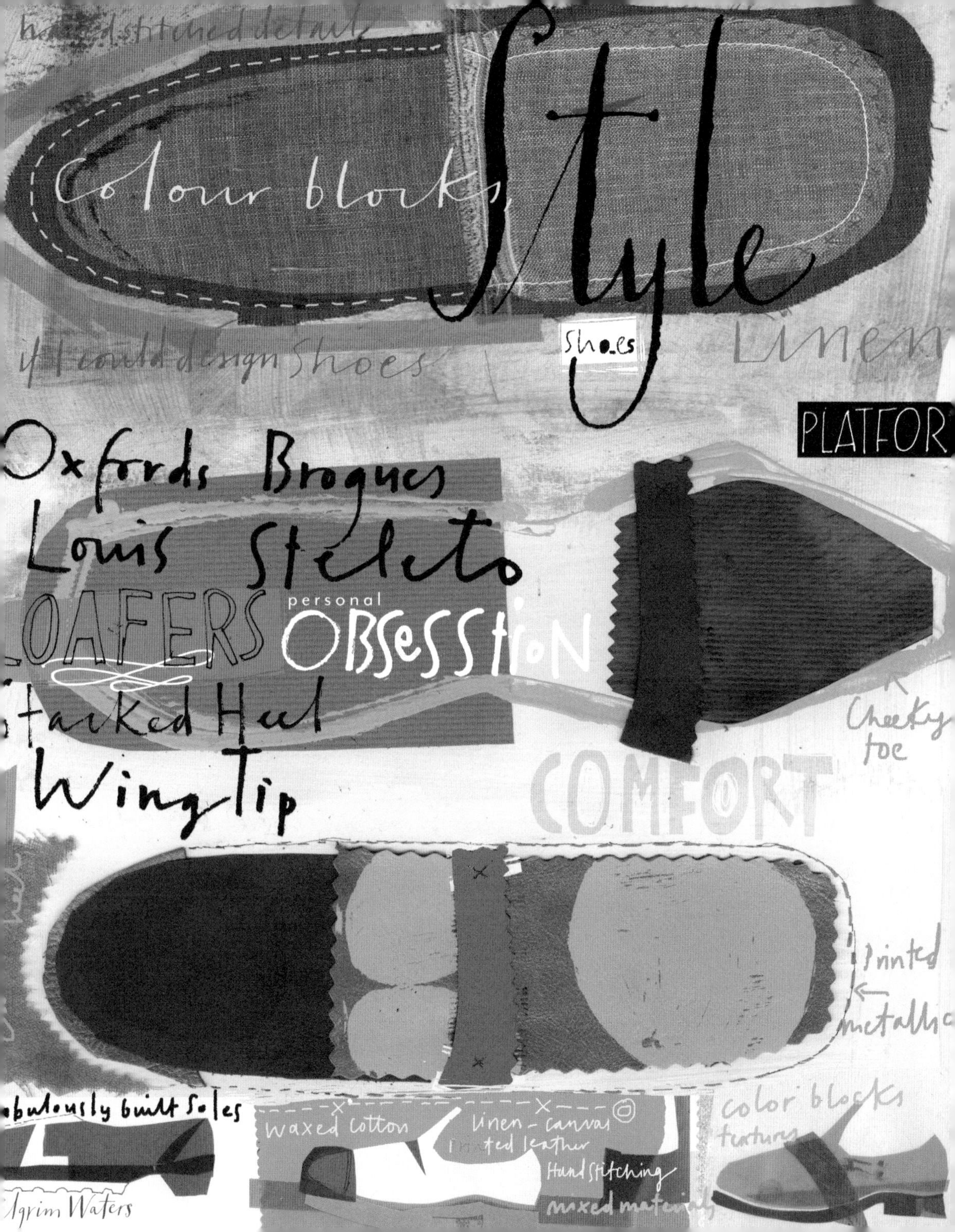

hand stitched details

Colour blocks, *Style*

if I could design shoes

shoes

Linen

PLATFOR

Oxfords Brogues
Louis Stelcto
LOAFERS personal OBSESSION
Stacked Heel
WingTip

COMFORT

Cheeky toe

Printed
metallic

fabulously built soles

waxed cotton

linen - canvas
coated leather
Hand stitching
mixed materials

color blocks
texture

Pilgrim Wafers

Keely Reyes

SAN FRANCISCO, USA

keelyreyes@gmail.com • @monkeyandwhale
keelyreyes.com • monkeyandthewhale.com

" I have a lot of quirky ideas that pop into my head," proclaims Keely Reyes. "That's what I love drawing most." She describes the instance of getting an idea onto paper as a "kismet moment."

"I'm very quirky, whimsical and imaginative. I think my personal work comes from a unique place. My imagination still lives in a childlike place, and that shows in a lot of my work."

Keely, her husband and their two children live in San Francisco, a city with no shortage of inspiration at hand. "The world around us is teeming with visual wonders, it would be hard not to find something inspiring. Nature and San Francisco itself always have things to offer."

"I like to draw at home, but when the kids are around I need to work elsewhere. Coffee shops are great for the coffee and treats. I recently joined a co-working space for other creative freelancers called Makeshift Society. It can be lonely on your own, so it is nice to get out and be with other like-minded individuals."

Musing on what she'd be if she weren't an illustrator, Keely says she could see herself as a food critic. "I think I have been watching too many food shows. That combined with my love for eating means my imagination has gotten away from me!"

THE ASSIGNMENT

Incorporating your handlettering with illustration, document an afternoon spent sketching and listening in a coffee shop, restaurant or another public space that you enjoy.

READY SET GO!
LIFE all AROUND
LOOK around
SEE WHAT YOU SEE
THINK
write
SKETCH
IDEAS
COLOR
light
SOUND
SET
FORTH
AND
RUN
A city TO inspire
Free

Jeff Rogers

BROOKLYN, USA

jeff@howdyjeff.com • @frogers
howdyjeff.com

" I was born, along with my identical twin brother, in Fort Worth, Texas. I grew up just north of Dallas, a baker's son. Another brother was born less than two years later and the three of us have been best friends ever since. I started drawing as soon as I could hold a pencil, and my grandmother taught me how to paint at a young age. She was a major influence on my life. In my younger years I dabbled in many forms of art, including tap dancing (yup), singing and theatre, as well as many sports. I found music at age 12 in the form of drums and percussion in the school band and devoted my life to it until my freshman year of college, when I decided I didn't want to be a band director (my perceived "only option") so I went back to my first love, art, and kept practicing and playing as much music as possible, which I still do.

I met my beautiful and amazing wife in 1999 and a year later discovered graphic design. I graduated with a graphic design degree and then I left to go on tour playing drums in a popular Texas country band. After marrying my sweetheart in 2004, I bounced around at different firms in Dallas.

In 2008 we moved to NYC and I got a job designing theatre posters at SpotCo where I learned what good typography was. I started drawing and painting type incessantly after hours. I put the work online as I made it. People liked it and I started getting calls for work doing lettering. So many calls started coming in that I left SpotCo in the summer of 2011 and I've been running my one-man studio ever since. **"**

THE ASSIGNMENT

Create an illustration and/or hand-lettered composition that riffs on the words and emotion of being a percussionist.

Michelle Romo

LOS ANGELES, USA

michelle@crowdedteeth.com • @monstromo
crowdedteeth.com

"I was born and raised in a small town in Southern California. I grew up seeing and loving cute things, and then one day I decided I wanted to make cute things for other people to see. My lovely family, friends, husband and cats were very supportive of my artistic endeavours. Now I get to draw cute things for a living!

I am pretty lucky. I have a split schedule: I have a steady design job that I have been with for nine years, working three days a week, and the rest of my freelance or personal work is done at home. I am very happy with my schedule and the direction of my career. I feel like I have the stability of a full-time job, and I get to choose who I say yes to as far as freelancing goes.

I live in Los Angeles and feel like I should stay here because of work. Being an artist affects the state of messiness in my home. It's a disaster half the time because when I am prepping for a show I am usually building stuff on my desk or dining room table or anywhere I can find space. My husband is very understanding of my sleepless nights and piles of 'art.'

In general I always say my style is influenced by both of my grandmas. My grandparents on my mom's side would visit every other summer from Japan. They would bring me a pile of cute things that I would get to paw through. My grandparents on my dad's side had a mid-century vibe to their house, which I spent a lot of time in. When I am in need of inspiration I travel down both of those paths."

THE ASSIGNMENT

Interpret a family tree of graphical and visual inspirations, showing how your grandmothers, family, pop culture and experience have informed your style.

Hannah Sawtell

NOTTINGHAM, UK

hannah.sawtell@ntlworld.com • @hannah_jaine
hannahsawtell.co.uk

" I started life in the Norfolk countryside—the land of beautiful skylines. My parents and I moved to the West Country to be near my Granny, and from there I moved to Nottingham to study contemporary arts. While taking my degree I met my future husband, although at the time we were 'just good friends.' A short period of not knowing what to do next resulted in me becoming an art teacher, after which a daughter, a marriage and a son shook things up a bit and I began investing more and more time into my love of drawing.

From an early age I loved to draw. Inspired by my mum showing me how to look and draw observationally, I began an ongoing process of keeping sketchbooks, documenting aspects of my life. Despite my degree being very conceptual, I kept returning to the joy of drawing, which was still a vital part of my creative process.

Being an illustrator is like being a magpie: selecting elements from the world around you (be they the environment, books, magazines or gallery visits) to inspire you on your own creative journey.

When working on an illustration, I can control composition and use of colour, but my drawing style is something I don't have much control over. Drawing is like handwriting: unique to the person making those marks on paper—and that is what makes me different. "

THE ASSIGNMENT

The use of photographic colour and textures in your line work is quite unique. Using this technique, imagine you are a magpie flying through the city. What would you draw?

Karolin Schnoor

LONDON, UK

hello@karolinschnoor.co.uk • @karolinschnoor
karolinschnoor.co.uk

" I was actually very academic at school and decided to go to art school as some sort of late teenage act of rebellion," admits Karolin Schnoor. "It wasn't really rebellious because my parents were very supportive! My foundation degree really got me interested in illustration, and I think my love of books certainly helped as well." Originally from Berlin, Karolin moved to London to pursue her illustration degree. "Ten years later I am still in London, working from a little studio south of the river and screen printing on the weekends."

Unlike some illustrators who dislike the business aspect of a freelance career, Karolin appreciates the balance between the practical and the creative. "I actually enjoy the commercial aspect of illustration. I like to think of it in a strategic way and I don't mind all the admin required. I couldn't focus only on creating; it would be much too stressful."

Her work is informed by the silkscreening process, favouring flat colours. "I have a few recurring themes that always find their way into my drawings, mainly women, plants and patterns. I think of all my illustrations in a very two-dimensional way. I like to break it down into areas of colour and shape and make sure the balance is right."

Her list of clients includes *The New York Times*, *The Telegraph* and *Time Out London*. "I'd love to do packaging and I'd also be interested in working with textiles or wallpaper designs," she says. "There's nothing better than having made something you're happy with, and if there's also a happy client involved then that's even better."

THE ASSIGNMENT

Create a self-portrait in which you are contrasted or camouflaged with one of your textiles or wallpaper designs.

Diana Schoenbrun

BROOKLYN, USA

dianaschoenbrun@gmail.com • @dianaschoenbrun
DianaSchoenbrun.net

PHOTOS BY TORY WILLIAMS

Diana Schoenbrun is a published author, having penned and illustrated two craft books, one on making softies inspired by cryptozoology and another on making puppets from recycled materials. She loves exaggeration, humour and the tactile, so it is not surprising that Diana often freelances at a puppet studio. "I recently travelled to Prague to learn Czech marionette puppet building and performance," she says.

"I became an illustrator because I love creating, drawing and making things with my hands. I am interested in the process of communicating abstract ideas visually. The challenge is to artistically communicate characters and stories with which people can connect," she says. "I enjoy drawing animals and people. Maybe I need to do a mixture of the two?"

In addition to more traditional painted and drawn imagery, Diana has a unique three-dimensional approach to image-making that combines scenic painting with construction and sewing. "I use colours and materials for which I have a personal affinity. I strive to create worlds that I would want to live in or that would interest me. I always try to convey a story. Character, personality and narrative are important."

Living in New York also provides an endless source of inspiration. "There are so many people and animals, and so much architecture to draw," she says: "Stimulation overload."

THE ASSIGNMENT

Imagining your dream assignment of illustrating a picture book, design the main character of the book as soft sculpture: a charismatic cat living in NYC who thinks he/she is a human.

Will Scobie

BRIGHTON, UK

hey@willscobie.co.uk • @will_scobie
willscobie.co.uk • willscobie.tumblr.com

Will Scobie is based in Brighton, the town in the south of England in which he was born. He's always had a fascination with drawing: "Drawing has always been a big part of my life. I studied communication design, which set good foundations for forming ideas and composition within graphic design. Once I graduated I decide to pursue drawing more, which eventually grew and evolved into my own illustration style."

Will has a unique graphic style, characterized by unending lines that loop in and around a subject, creating a framework that defines as much as it abstracts. "My approach to illustration plays with the idea of the continuous line, whilst maintaining a graphic simplicity and communicating an idea through a playful and optimistic perspective."

"My main inspiration is nature, with its infinite shapes and colours to draw from. Lately I seem to have an obsession with nature, particularly creatures of the sea and their organic flow and form. But I also like to delve into research for each project, to pick up on all the intricacies and details of the subject."

"Drawing is a part of my everyday life. I like to take a sketchbook everywhere I go. My work and my life feed into each other. I gain inspiration from the things around me but I am also constantly drawing from my imagination."

THE ASSIGNMENT

You state: "My work and my life feed into each other." With your fluid continuous line style, show this relationship with a visual metaphor.

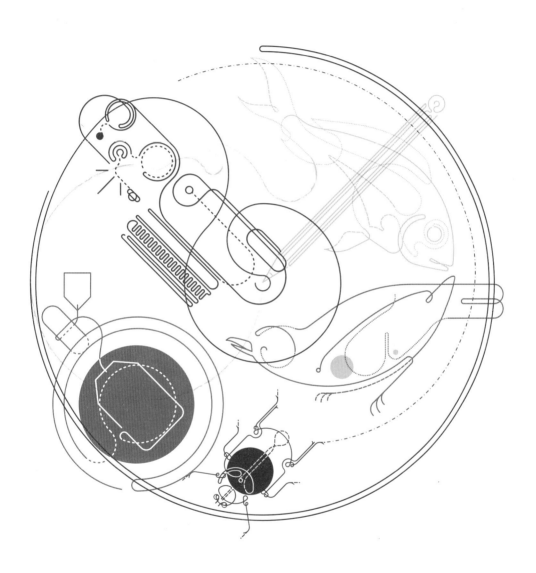

Ann Shen

LOS ANGELES, USA

annlashen@gmail.com • @anndanger
ann-shen.com • shopannshen.etsy.com

" I was born and raised in the suburbs of southern California. I attended UC San Diego where I studied writing, film and photography. Shortly after graduating, I moved to LA where I spent several years working for non-profits by day and reading design blogs and making paintings by night.

I always wanted to be an artist but was steered toward a more practical route by my pragmatic parents, who didn't want me living with them for the rest of their lives. But after doing all the things I was supposed to do—such as graduating from a good liberal arts university—I was unhappy. My boyfriend was in art school at the time, and I looked at what he was working on and said, "I want to do that!"

With the encouragement of my family and friends, I made the leap and went back to school at Art Center College of Design. Now I work as an in-house designer and a freelance illustrator.

My work is joyful, full of colour and grounded in mid-century children's book and fashion illustration, always with a wink.

When you're doing something you love, your work is your life and your life is your work— it's inextricably intertwined and I wouldn't want it any other way. Being an artist and a creative person is not just a job but part of who I am. "

PHOTOS BY CHRISTINA WINKELMANN

THE ASSIGNMENT

Illustrate one item that you love—be it food, clothing, an object—for each colour of the rainbow.

Cheers!

Salut!

Erica Sirotich

SAN FRANCISCO, USA

ericasirotich@gmail.com • @cuddlefishpress
ericasirotich.com • cuddlefishpress.com

" I am starting to learn that I am a bit more Type A or perhaps OCD than a lot of other illustrators," confesses Erica Sirotich from her home studio in San Francisco. "As much as I adore illustrations that have a messy, loose quality, I can't seem to make them myself. I draw and redraw or ink and re-ink pieces obsessively until they are exactly what I envisioned. I obsess over detail and line quality especially."

Erica's attention to detail results in quality work: "In the digital arena I create illustration files with meticulously, sensibly ordered layers. My invoices and expense records are neat and tidy. The prints I create for my shop, Cuddlefish Press, each have their own drawer in the flat files and are oh-so-carefully packaged. My studio, though nearly overflowing with books, paper and supplies, is orderly and organized. I'm like the accountant of the illustration world."

That is, an accountant who draws quirky, funny characters. "But I think, in general, people don't take you as seriously when they find out you draw kittens and jellyfish and astronauts for a living."

"My number one goal is to illustrate children's picture books. That would be my dream assignment. But I'd like to get involved in other aspects of the children's market, too—illustrating for magazines, games, paper goods, maps, stickers, apparel and other children's products."

THE ASSIGNMENT

Create a sweet and silly activity book page for the 9-year-old version of yourself. Fill it with things you loved then and now. Include yourself in the illustration.

RUBBISH ROUND UP

Captain Soggypaddles' crew has been at sea for weeks and has amassed lots of trash. Help them sort and deliver it to the correct rubbish professional and keep the ocean clean!

TODD'S TOXIC WASTE DISPOSAL

POUR COMPOSTABLES HERE

RUDY'S RECYCLING

4¢ REFUND

GULPY'S COMPOST CENTER

Katie Skau

BROOKLYN, USA

katieskau@gmail.com • @katieskau
katieskau.com • katieskau.wordpress.com

K atie Skau's subject matter makes for an enticing list: "girls with long hair, patterns, most animals, foliage, plant life and fairy tales." Katie sees herself in her portfolio. "I think that many of my characters are already self-portraits," she says, "but I have never created one intentionally."

Katie hand-cuts her illustrations using an X-Acto knife and then embellishes them with mixed media. "I primarily use paper, fabric, thread, paint and wood, but I am not opposed to any media that will help illustrate the piece I am working on." The resulting illustration, whether conceived as a flat surface or a diorama with depth, can be described as a sort of contemporary folk art with Victorian influences.

"Each cut or stitch or stroke I place into my work is part of me and a calculated piece of my vision and personal creativity. The best thing about being an illustrator is having a creative outlet to explore your emotions and build something out of nothing. The worst thing is that the intense motivation you need to succeed can sometimes interfere with your personal life and relationships."

Katie is currently based in New York City, where she balances a day job as a graphic designer with a burgeoning illustration career. "Though I can really work anywhere that has a hard surface and a cutting mat, I do work in a home studio. Eventually it may be nice to have a bit of separation, though."

THE ASSIGNMENT

Envision your own folklore or fairy tale and make a self-portrait in which elements of you (ie your hair, limbs, clothes and/or body) depict the story.

Linda Solovic

SAINT LOUIS, USA

lsolovic@mindspring.com
behance.net/lindasolovic • lindasolovic.etsy.com

" **M**y style combines all sorts of stuff into one picture: fabric, embellishments, charms, trinkets and ephemera. I put little touches into my illustrations to delight people.

When I create my illustrations I like to focus on several things: the balance of positive and negative space, how one shape fits into another or affects another and the balance of light and dark. I love to work with colour to make my images come alive, especially with colour palettes that are unexpected or that others might shy away from (I especially love ugly yellow-greens). I also love to play with pattern, using pattern on top of pattern to see just how much I can use and still have the illustration hold together. I like to see just how much busyness I can add to an image and still have it work.

I love to go junking at estate sales and flea markets, where I pick up all kinds of stuff to use in my work.

So many things inspire me: odd colour palettes, mid-century modern textiles, furniture, children's illustration, vintage fabric, greeting cards, gift wrap, home decor magazines, going to antique malls and junk sales, things with a patina to them, typography, hand lettering, embellishments like old odd jewelry, ribbon, buttons, charms, old ephemera, quilts, crafts like plushies, needle felting, embroidery, other illustrators whose work I admire, travelling to odd places like roadside attractions and outsider art installations, Japanese kawaii and children's toys and games. I could go on and on. "

THE ASSIGNMENT

Show your love of haberdashery (ribbons, buttons, thread, etc) and your hobby of quilting and stitching by creating a series of spot illustrations for a book about sewing.

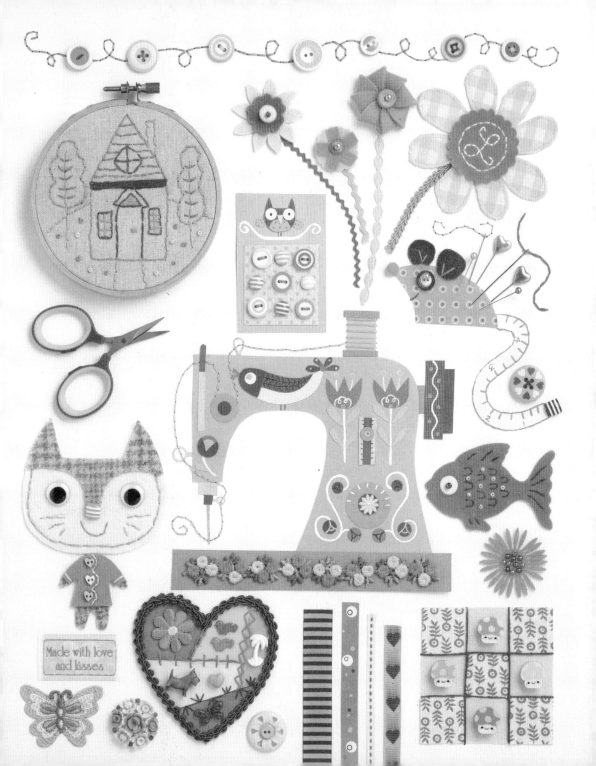

Made with love
and kisses

Carey Sookocheff

TORONTO, CANADA

info@careysookocheff.com • @careysookocheff
careysookocheff.com

Like many women, Carey Sookocheff had to put her career on pause to focus on her family. "I worked as an illustrator for about eight years until I had my first daughter, Harper, in 2006. In 2008 we had our second daughter, Edie. I worked a bit here and there, but mostly I looked after the kids." Now that her children are in school, Carey is getting back to her work.

"Having children simply means I'm not available to work as many hours of the day as I used to be. Also, taking time off when my kids were little meant that I really stepped away from illustration for a long time. I lost clients and I lost my name in the business. I very much feel like I'm starting from scratch again in terms of getting my name and my work back out there."

Her linocut illustrations and calm colour palettes are quite distinctive yet reflect a humble process of cutting and carving. "The linoleum I'm using right now is from the offcuts from the floor we had installed in our hallway."

With clear and clever concepts, clients will welcome Carey's return to freelance. "I like to keep my ideas clean and smart and to the point. I always want my illustrations to make the audience think, too."

"The best thing about being an illustrator," explains Carey, "is that I get to make images. I enjoy reading articles and being exposed to ideas that I would probably not be in another career. The range of assignments that we work on as illustrators is really great."

THE ASSIGNMENT

Illustrate the cover of a children's book about you and your relationship with your two daughters.

Here
is our
Garden

Caileigh Speck

VANCOUVER, CANADA

hello@caileighspeck.com • @caileighspeck
caileighspeck.com

" I love the feeling of creating and telling stories through my work," says Caileigh Speck. "I love that I can do for a living what I feel like I was meant to do. It sounds cliché but honestly the joy and happiness you get from sharing something that you've created is unbelievable!" And the worst thing about being an illustrator? "It's hard!" she says. "Putting yourself out there is so scary. Your income is not steady, which is a little terrifying."

Caileigh came to illustration by way of photography and design. "Everything I learned helped me focus on promoting myself as a graphic designer while working away at improving my illustration." Her colourful gouache, watercolour, ink and pencil drawings are full of patterns, natural motifs and a positive spirit. "I embrace imperfections. No one can draw exactly like me and I appreciate the nuances in my work that set me apart."

"I really want to get into the nooks and crannies of what I'm working on. I want to find some unknown fact or secret or something hidden and really bring that out and explore it as much as I can. I love getting lost in creating forests of flowers and leaves and pattern."

Caileigh also explores other crafts, such as knitting and crochet. "I think these help because they expand my creative thinking and keep it dimensional." Viewers can liken the organized busyness of Caileigh's floral patterns with the intricacies of a knitted sweater. Both are warm, cosy and colourful.

THE ASSIGNMENT

Lose yourself in creating a forest of flowers, leaves and pattern. Select plants, colours and linework that express who you are and what you love.

Marta Spendowska

GREEN BAY, USA

contact@martaspendowska.com • @martaspendowska
martaspendowska.com

" I've drawn all my life, but I've never thought about being an artist. You don't have that kind of dream in post-communist Poland. After attending a few universities and working a dead-end job, I decided to leave my old life behind and hop on a plane to the United States. Having experienced America while completing an internship in Atlanta, Georgia, during my senior year at university, I knew it was the place for me to be and do something creative.

I sold my first painting in Atlanta while sitting on the pavement, across from a Whole Foods. That was the moment when I realized how possible it might be to pursue a life as an artist in the US. I went back to Poland, finished my degree, hopped on a plane two years later and started a new life.

I sketch in watercolour. The nature of the medium dictates the final feel and I like to jump into it. It doesn't have the polished look, but it's easier for me to sketch and share it this way. Portraits are my favourite things to draw. I've drawn portraits of prominent Communists since my childhood (based on ugly calendars) and since then I've been moved by faces. I paint a lot of portraits of complicated women, like Leonora Carrington and Virginia Woolf. I love the multiple dimensions of women characters. I also love painting perfume bottles and other objects. "

THE ASSIGNMENT

Paint a portrait of yourself as the complicated woman you are, either twenty years into the future or twenty years in the past. Use the stylistic qualities of watercolour to convey the emotion of the life ahead or the life lived.

Marta describes her portrait: "Whenever I close my eyes I see myself in Paris, working in a high ceiling studio, with a baguette and a strong espresso on the side. It's Paris and it has an attitude, like the old French movie stars or French women inspired by Sartorialist. They all smoke and it's a part of the French energy. Personally I can't stand the smoke, but in Paris I might just fall in love with it."

Studio SSS

HUDSON, USA & BENNINGTON, USA

salli@studiosss.com • nate@studiosss.com
studiosss.com • idrawmaps.com

" **S**tudio SSS is myself, Salli Swindell, and Nate Padavick. We are a brother and sister design and illustration team. Nate was born when I was in junior high so I didn't pay too much attention to him until decades later, when I realized he could teach me some computer skills! Our lives meandered along very different paths until one day we found ourselves together in my studio, realizing we might make a good design team. I planted roots in a big home in a small town with my husband and began a freelance career after our two boys were born. Meanwhile, Nate and his boyfriend travelled the world, always moving from one great city to the next with bikes and suitcases in tow. Fortunately, video chats and lots of coffee make it easy to keep our business alive!

People often respond to our work by saying, "It looks like you had fun creating this!" That is by far the best compliment we could possibly receive. Designing and illustrating make us happy and we're glad it shows!

We launched our websites They Draw & Cook and They Draw & Travel partly as an international playground for artists everywhere to have some fun and share their talents with the world. And the best part? Artists have received tons of work by being spotted on our sites.

Around the time that we came up with the concept for They Draw & Cook, I suppose I was in my studio more than I realized, and one day my teenage son came into the studio and said, "Hey Mom, how 'bout a little less drawing and a little more cooking?" "

THE ASSIGNMENT

Make a creative map of the people, places and things that inspire you as an illustrator. Please divide the available space in two for each of your illustrations but plan to join the images (ie lines or a road from one leading into another).

Benoit Tardif

MONTREAL, CANADA

info@bentardif.com
bentardif.com • benoittardif.tumblr.com

" I have been a hockey player ever since I was a kid," says Benoit Tardif. "It teaches me to persevere, which is an important quality for an illustrator."

Born in 1983 in a small Québécois town, Benoit studied graphic design in Montreal. Like hockey, he has loved drawing ever since he was a child. His professional illustration style melds a childlike sense of line and shape with a designer's eye. "My style is simple, colourful and efficient. I like to create great ideas that make people smile. Integrity is very important to me. I want to make images that reflect 100 percent of my personality."

Ben's inspirations include "big cities, old taverns, fast foods, hockey cards, American folk art and master illustrators like Seymour Chwast, Saul Steinberg and Jim Flora." He lives in Montreal with his wife. "I made the choice to live in Montreal because there is more opportunity for an artist here than in a small town. I need to live in a big city because it inspires me a lot." When he feels distracted by things at home, Ben heads to a café to work.

Ben's dream clients include *Monocle*, *Nobrow* and the Montreal Canadiens.

THE ASSIGNMENT

Drawing upon your personal experience and love of hockey, make an illustration that pokes fun at the stereotype of Canada and its national pastime, hockey.

Dan Bob Thompson

BURBANK, USA

danbobthompson@gmail.com
danbobthompson.com

Dan Bob Thompson grew up in Los Angeles, surfed a lot, received a BFA in animation from CalArts and was recruited by Disney. After working at Disney for nearly a decade, Dan switched studios and worked for the Cartoon Network as a character artist. Now following his dream of freelancing full time, he illustrates for publishing, greeting cards and animation studios.

His work has a retro flair, especially noticeable in the styling of his lines. "I really like colour and bold shapes with a bit of texture," he says. "I also love filigree and I always try to find a place for it." His favourite subject matter includes the circus, the sea and cats.

His home life is optimized for creative time. "I have a lovely wife and a special basset hound named Bella. My wife and I are both artists and art is all we do. I work from home and I tend to get lost in an assignment and work way too many hours on it," Dan says. "I usually start my day around 5:30 am and work to 3 pm. Then I get out of the house and go for a hike." Still, he does take time to relax: "We really make an effort to see a movie, though, or sit on the couch after 9 pm."

Dan's dream assignment would be to illustrate a Bukowski story.

THE ASSIGNMENT

You've stated that you love to draw cats, the circus and the sea. What would happen if two of these things—or all three!—were combined and you starred as the ringmaster? (Wrangling cats on a sea circus sounds like a metaphor for an illustration career...)

Ekaterina Trukhan

LONDON, UK

e.trukhan@gmail.com
ekaterinatrukhan.com

Since graduating from the Camberwell College of Arts in London, Russian-born Ekaterina Trukhan has been developing her career as a children's book author and illustrator, as well as creating editorial illustration for books, magazines and greeting cards.

"I work from home and usually start early in the morning with a cup of coffee. I work at my desk, listening to music, but when I'm coming up with ideas or making sketches, I prefer to move about and find a comfortable armchair or sofa to sit at and draw. I normally try to finish my work around late afternoon or before it gets dark, as I don't like to work at night."

Her work is full of light with soft yet bright colours, often depicting happy children. "My style is naïve and slightly nostalgic," describes Ekaterina. "I like mid-century illustration and its colour palette. I'm also quite influenced by Soviet animation and picture books, which are part of my background."

Ekaterina feels close to her work: images that keep her in touch with her inner child and offer comfort when she is blue. "I share my personality traits and appearance with most of my characters, which often happens subconsciously. Each of them can be considered my self-portrait."

THE ASSIGNMENT

Draw a series of pictures showing you doing things that make you happy throughout the day.

Valesca van Waveren

AMSTERDAM, THE NETHERLANDS

mail@valezki.com • @valezki
valezki.com

" After high school I couldn't decide to either go to art school or use my good grades for something studious. I chose psychology at first and then on the weekends I took a basic art course at the Gerrit Rietveld Academie in Amsterdam. I continued with developmental psychology, which I liked very much. I joined the university magazine to make illustrations and to write. It was there that I found out it was important to pursue my dreams. I enrolled in the art academy and became an illustrator. My studio, Valezki, began five years ago.

I like drawing objects in general, more than people. I love to draw things with buttons and mechanical stuff, such as typewriters, cameras or electricity stations and such.

I aspire to make work that is communicative, humorous, sometimes melancholic, honest, surprising and colourful. Hopefully I inspire people to question normality, to embrace imperfections, to find treasures in what seems to be boring. But in my heart I think the reason that I am an illustrator has something to do with the need to tell a clear story: to have the time to think about how to tell what you want to tell. In 'real life,' conversation-wise, I am always a bit fearful of being misinterpreted, or being boring, or saying something I meant to put differently.

My father, who died in April last year, was a big collector of anything you can imagine. Going through all his stuff was an immense project. But now a lot of really nice things of his, such as vintage tin cans, lamps, boxes, a candy machine, a nice chair and more are in our house. This makes me very happy every day. I felt somehow that this would be the nicest thing I could draw. "

THE ASSIGNMENT

Drawing upon your love of illustrating collections, depict some objects that have personal significance.

Lauren Venell

SAN FRANCISCO, USA

lauren@venell.me • @lvenell
laurenvenell.com

Lauren Venell's work is eclectic. From a human-sized, silver 'Bold Burrito' costume, to a wreath made of recycled credit cards, to soft plush pillows representing cuts of meats, Lauren's work is certainly not limited by its materials, nor by Lauren's imagination.

"I use whatever medium satisfies the assignment best," she explains. "Though I tend to use paper, fabric and clay most often, since they are so open-ended and flexible, I have also created props and illustrations using electronics, stickers, apples, credit cards and office supplies. As my husband once said, 'all anyone has to do to solve their design problem is set you loose in a hardware store.'"

The diversity in material selection may be related to her circuitous path to illustration. "Always hungry to learn new skills, I have worked in many fields and media over the years, including education, toy design, advertising, computer science and marine biology. Far from being unrelated, each experience has enlightened the next, and I am extremely grateful to have work that stimulates and challenges me every day."

"I have been an artist for as long as I can remember. Though at times I have made my living in other ways, it is through art that I solve problems and create meaning in my life. Making art allows me to combine all of my skills and interests, so every day is different and exciting. Some days I spend my time on research, brainstorming or critical thinking, while others may be spent on quiet and meditative production work, like cutting paper or carving linoleum."

Lauren creates "artifacts of contemporary culture." In making things in three dimensions, her work tends to be viewed differently than traditional illustration. The object demands attention and close examination. "My work plays on the tension between our childish desire to play and learn, and our adult, consumerist desire to collect and admire."

THE ASSIGNMENT

Go to the hardware store, a grocery store or a flea market and select some objects to use in an assemblage or composition about you.

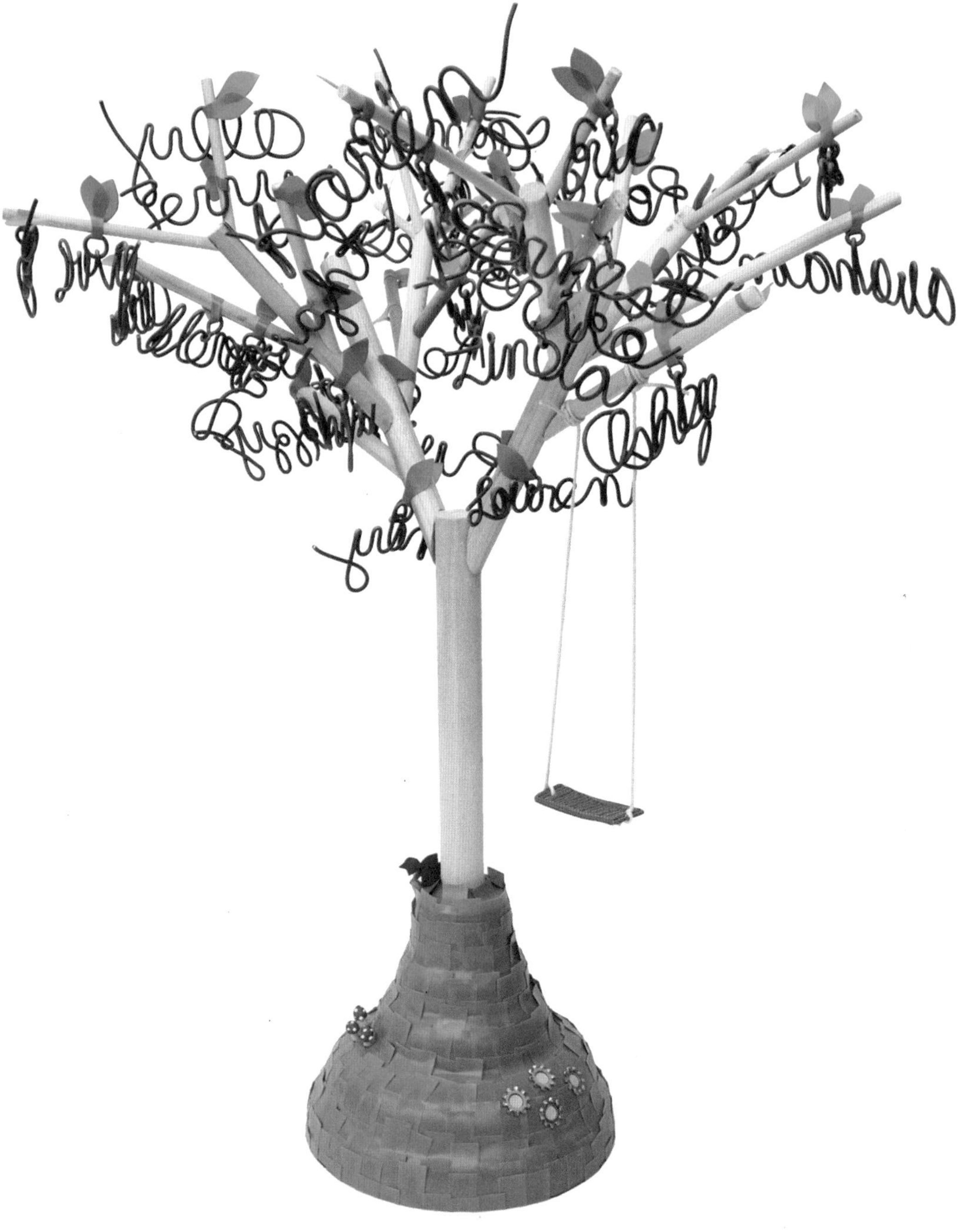

Lea Vervoort

BREDA, THE NETHERLANDS

info@leavervoort.nl • @lea_vervoort
leavervoort.nl

" I was cheerful, shy and a little dreamer with a big imagination," says Dutch illustrator Lea Vervoort of herself as a child. "I grew up in a small, peaceful and slightly boring town in the south of the Netherlands. After high school I moved to the city and studied illustration at a beautiful Dutch art academy. I graduated last summer. Now I'm busy setting up my little illustration business and showing my illustrations to the world."

Lea shares a home studio with her boyfriend, an animator who also works from home. "It's quite nice to have the company of another creative soul," says Lea. Though at some point when funds allow she'd love to have a separate studio. "Illustration is a really big part of my life. It's my passion and it's my work. And even if I'm not working I'm thinking about it, so there's not really a balance between work and life here. But I don't mind, it makes me happy."

Lea's drawings are done in mechanical pencil, which she then scans, using Photoshop to add colour and texture. "Working digitally gives me, as a perfectionist, opportunities to easily cut and paste pieces of my illustration, change colour and add or undo things if I want to."

"Sometimes I'm still a kid who thinks that grown-ups are boring. With my work I hope to surprise and bring back a little sparkle to dusty lives."

THE ASSIGNMENT

Draw your ideal house in cross-section, showing your favourite rooms and the perfect home studio.

Carl Wiens

PICTON, CANADA

wiens@kos.net • @carlwiens
carlwiens.com • illoz.com/carlw

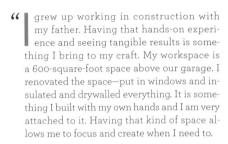

" I grew up working in construction with my father. Having that hands-on experience and seeing tangible results is something I bring to my craft. My workspace is a 600-square-foot space above our garage. I renovated the space—put in windows and insulated and drywalled everything. It is something I built with my own hands and I am very attached to it. Having that kind of space allows me to focus and create when I need to.

I have two sons. Raising them has been a real challenge, but I have become very focused over the years and use my time wisely. Seeing the world through their eyes opens up so many new possibilities. Living where I work lets me be incredibly close to them and stay involved in their lives. I feel very fortunate to share both worlds.

Time spent away from the studio is critical. I stay productive when I can get out to cycle or go to the beach or go on a canoe trip. I usually build an ice rink behind the studio every winter for my kids. It keeps me from getting cabin fever. If I don't have that balance I get diminishing returns on my efforts. You have to recharge, and the best way is to dive into something completely different.

I have been doing this for over 24 years. I still wake up every day and try to develop something new, to bring in something I haven't tried before. My work keeps evolving and growing. "

THE ASSIGNMENT

Illustrate the construction of your studio above the garage, taking creative liberties to enhance the story and emotional/personal impact of the piece.

Brad Woodard

AUSTIN, USA

hello@bravethewoods.com • @bradwwoodard
bravethewoods.com • dribbble.com/bradwwoodard

B rad Woodard is a young dad, husband, full-time designer and freelance illustrator. "I don't sleep. Ever," he says. He would like to transition to being solely self-employed, a plan that involves the cooperation of the whole family.

"I have a one-year-old little boy, and my freelance business is booming more than ever. All my nights and weekends are taken up by my freelance work. My wife is great. She has helped me schedule out all of my work."

"I have to sacrifice quite a bit, taking on as much freelance illustration work as I do right now. Luckily I have the most understanding and supportive wife. She makes it possible for me to be able to work after I come home from my full-time job."

Brad has lived in quite a few different cities. "My creative mind never takes a break. It is a problem. As a result, I tend to move a lot. And the places I like to move to are generally beautiful, hence my living in Seattle, the Philippines, Newport Beach and Boston."

He and his young family have recently relocated to Austin, Texas, where Brad will be concentrating on growing his company, Brave The Woods.

"My dream illustration assignment would be to illustrate a children's science book. That, or illustrate the side of a U-Haul truck."

THE ASSIGNMENT

You've stated that the best thing about being an illustrator is that "you have the chance to interpret the world around you and visualize it how you see it." With that in mind, illustrate an idealized road-trip, and/or depict your life as the graphics on the side of a U-Haul trailer.

Janice Wu

VANCOUVER, CANADA

janicelkwu@gmail.com
janice-wu.com

" I was born and raised in Vancouver, British Colum-
bia, the land of beautiful mountains, lakes and delicious, cheap sushi. I knew I wanted to be an artist
ever since I was little. One of my earliest memories of
making art was this phase I went through in elementary
school where I was obsessed with the Sanrio character
Pochacco, a white dog with floppy ears that could play
basketball. I would draw him constantly! When I was
around eight, I started a little recess business by making Pochacco drawings and selling them for a penny
each. One day, this wise guy from an older grade came
up to me and offered me a dollar for a hundred pictures!
Needless to say it was a very long night of frantic drawing! It's been a while since then. I just graduated with
a BFA from Emily Carr University of Art & Design and
my illustration career is in its exciting beginnings.

Every time I am approached by a client for illustration
work, I am surprised, flattered and incredibly humbled.
Working as an illustrator has given me confidence in
my work and style, which is something that took me
a long time to discover. It has given me affirmation
and it is what keeps me motivated as an artist to continue creating.

I see my creative vision as parallel to the ways in which
a botanist creates meticulous, detailed drawings of
flora in order to observe and understand them, or how a
field scientist plucks specimen from nature and places
them in stark, white laboratories for study and contem-
plation. My practice investigates overlooked fragments
and material traces of our daily existence, bringing up
larger questions surrounding value, and the manner
in which we determine what is precious or disposable.
What does it mean to slowly and painstakingly render a
receipt in high realism, something that is so mindlessly
crumpled up and thrown away? I'm interested in shift-
ing our perceptions on what is considered mundane,
and doing so in poetic and playful ways. "

THE ASSIGNMENT

*Document a day in your life through a meticulous rendering
of the things usually ignored and tossed, such as wrappers,
receipts, packaging and containers.*

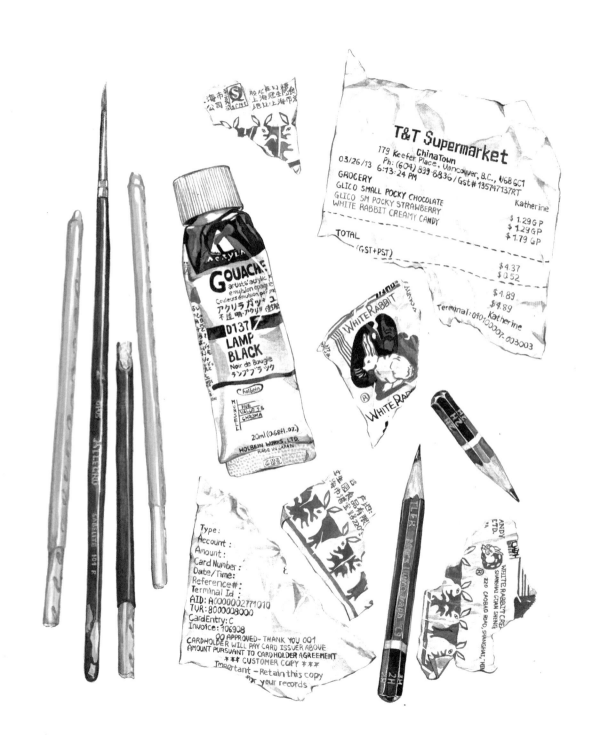

Debra Ziss

BROOKLYN, USA

missziss@gmail.com • @missziss
debraziss.com • debbiedoesdoodles.com

D ebra Ziss loves hanging out with her dogs in her Brooklyn home studio. "Chihuahuas make excellent studio mates! On my left is my dog Francie, who sits atop my desk. On my right, I have what has been affectionately referred to as my hobo corner. The hobo corner is a mess and I have to pretend it's not there if I want to get any work done."

"Because most of my work is assignment-driven, I prefer to think of myself as a pair of hired hands. It's my job as an illustrator to translate my client's vision through my talents and abilities. However, anything that features a dashiki-clad dog speaking French has been drawn purely for my personal enjoyment," she jests.

Debra enjoys keeping sketchbooks as part of her creative development. "My reportage sketchbook is for those rare times when I get a seat on the subway and I'm able to record my fellow passengers. Another is used for life drawing, and yet another is where I practice hand lettering. While these sketches don't resemble my commercial work, I love them because they're a raw, unfiltered look at life."

She enjoys the freedom that being an illustrator provides. ("I could do this job from a yak farm in Mongolia as long as they have electricity and WiFi. Thank you, Internet!")

Debra describes her ideal day succinctly: "massage, tacos, puppies, repeat." If she wasn't an illustrator, you'd find her employed as a dog groomer, epidemiologist, Zumba instructor, brewmaster or cheesemonger.

THE ASSIGNMENT

Imagine that your dogs live in a townhouse and invite you over to visit.

UPPERCASE

SHELLEY DAVIES

SARAH BRIDGLAND

GREG LAMARCHE

UPPERCASE publishes books and magazines for the creative and curious: products that spark the imagination and inspire creativity. Our eponymous magazine, launched in 2009, is loved by readers around the world and has been recognized for its design excellence. Our books profile up-and-coming artists or explore emerging trends in design and creativity.

We view everything we publish as an opportunity to create something special, so each product has high production values and attention to detail. A playful exploration of creativity, an affinity for vintage ephemera and a love of typography are some elements common to many of our publications.

Visit our blog for daily inspiration and subscribe to receive our magazine in your home or office.

COMMISSION AN ILLUSTRATOR FROM WORK/LIFE 3 AND GET A SUBSCRIPTION DISCOUNT!

Share your project with us and receive a special discount coupon for the UPPERCASE online shop, valid on subscriptions, back issues and books!

janine@uppercasemagazine.com

3